新制多益

聽力 搶分訓練營

3 STEPS 打造 高效聽力腦

中譯解析本

U0069676

01 單人獨照   p.10

STEP 1 題型演練

1 (X)	2 (X)	3 (X)	4 (O)	5 (O)
6 (X)	7 (X)			

1 一名女子穿著正式套裝。
2 一名女子正穿上外套。
3 一名女子正在使用傳真機。
4 一名女子正按下影印機的按鈕。
5 一名女子正站在某項辦公室設備前面。
6 影印機卡紙了。
7 書籍堆放在地板上。

STEP 3 聽寫練習

1 (B) (D)	2 (A) (B)

1

(A) A man is holding a pen.
(B) A man is reaching for a telephone.
(C) A man is staring at a computer screen.
(D) A man is working at a desk.

(A) 一名男子拿著一枝筆。
(B) 一名男子正伸手拿起電話。
(C) 一名男子正盯著電腦螢幕看。
(D) 一名男子正坐在書桌前工作。

解析

照片中的男子坐在書桌前，伸手去拿電話。(B) 提到「reach for」(伸手拿)、(D)提到「work at a desk」(在書桌前工作)，故均為正確答案。

字彙 **reach for** 伸手去拿 (東西)
stare 盯著、凝視

2

(A) She is making food in the kitchen.
(B) She is wearing a pair of gloves.
(C) She is putting on an apron.
(D) She is carrying a tray.

(A) 她正在廚房作菜。
(B) 她戴著一副手套。
(C) 她正穿上圍裙。
(D) 她正拿著托盤。

解析

動詞 wear 表示穿戴的狀態，(B) 表示戴著手套，故為正確答案。「put on」描述穿上去的動作，因此 (C) 並不正確。

字彙 **put on** 穿上、戴上 (衣物) **apron** 圍裙
tray 托盤

實戰演練   p.12

1 (B)	2 (A)	3 (D)	4 (B)

1

(A) He is paying for some groceries.
(B) He is holding a basket.
(C) He is displaying merchandise on shelves.
(D) He is pushing a shopping cart.

(A) 他買了一些食品雜貨，正在付錢。
(B) 他正拿著一個籃子。
(C) 他正把商品排到貨架上。
(D) 他正推著一輛購物車。

解析

照片中的男子站在陳列架前方，手提籃子，因此答案選 (B)。其他選項中提到的「pay for」（付錢）、display（陳列）、push（推）皆與男子的動作無關。

字彙 grocery 食品雜貨
merchandise 商品、貨物

2

(A) A woman is looking into a microscope.
(B) A woman is wearing glasses.
(C) A woman is using a microphone.
(D) A woman is cleaning some laboratory equipment.

(A) 一名女子正在用顯微鏡進行觀察。
(B) 一名女子戴著眼鏡。
(C) 一名女子正在使用麥克風。
(D) 一名女子正在清潔某項實驗室設備。

解析

女子在實驗室內看著顯微鏡，因此答案為 (A)。microscope（顯微鏡）和 microphone（麥克風）的發音相似，請特別留意。

字彙 microscope 顯微鏡　laboratory 實驗室
equipment 設備、器材

3

(A) A man is washing a car with a hose.
(B) A man is fixing a car.
(C) A man is sweeping the road.
(D) A man is wearing a jacket.

(A) 一名男子正在用水管洗車。
(B) 一名男子正在修車。
(C) 一名男子正在清掃馬路。
(D) 一名男子穿著夾克。

解析

仔細觀看照片後，會發現男子正在用水管清洗道路，並非洗車，因此答案不能選 (A)；(C) sweep 指的是用掃把清掃，因此也不是答案；(D) 描寫男子穿著夾克，故為正確答案。

字彙 fix 修理　sweep 清掃

4

(A) She is arranging flowers.
(B) She is watering a potted plant.
(C) She is mowing the lawn.
(D) She is planting a tree.

(A) 她正在插花。
(B) 她正在給盆栽澆水。
(C) 她正在除草坪上的草。
(D) 她正在種樹。

解析

照片中的女子正在給盆栽內的植物澆水，因此答案為 (B)。(A)「arrange flowers」指的是「插花」、(C)「mow the lawn」指的是「除草」，因此皆不是答案；(D) 女子並非在種植樹木，因此該選項也不正確。

字彙 arrange flowers 插花
mow the lawn 除草坪的草

STEP 1 題型演練

1 (O)	2 (X)	3 (X)	4 (O)	5 (X)
6 (X)	7 (O)			

1 其中一名女子拿著一個檔案。
2 她們正彼此對著對方微笑。
3 這些女子正在開視訊會議。
4 她們兩人都穿著正式服裝。
5 她們彼此緊臨而坐。
6 一名女子正從口袋裡拿出筆記。
7 這些女子彼此面對面而坐。

STEP 3 聽寫練習

1 (B)	2 (B)

1

(A) The people are holding onto the railing.
(B) They are jogging along the river.
(C) Some people are exercising in the gym.
(D) The bridge is being built now.

(A) 人們正抓著欄杆。
(B) 他們正沿著河邊慢跑。
(C) 有些人正在健身房運動。
(D) （某人）現在正在修建橋樑。

解析

照片中的兩個人正沿著河岸邊慢跑，因此答案為 (B)。along 為介系詞，意思為「沿著」。請注意，雖然照片中有出現橋，但是千萬不要因為聽到 bridge 就誤選 (D) 作為答案。

字彙 railing 欄杆

2

(A) They are shopping in a department store.
(B) They are trying on shoes.
(C) They are stacking up shoes on the shelf.
(D) They are picking up shopping bags.

(A) 她們正在百貨公司購物。
(B) 她們正在試穿鞋子。
(C) 她們正把鞋子堆放在貨架上。
(D) 她們正拿起購物袋。

解析

畫面中的兩名女子正在試穿好幾雙鞋子，(B) 描寫她們「正在試穿鞋子」，故為正確答案。「try on」可以用來表達「試穿衣物或鞋子」。

字彙 try on 試穿　shelf 架子、貨架

實戰演練　　　　p.16

1 (B)	2 (B)	3 (A)	4 (C)

1

(A) The men are wearing glasses.
(B) The men are reviewing some documents.
(C) They are wearing casual clothes.
(D) They are looking out the window.

(A) 這些男子戴著眼鏡。
(B) 這些男子正在審閱一些文件。
(C) 他們穿著便服。
(D) 他們正看著窗外。

解析

照片中的兩名男子正一同檢視著文件。(B) 描寫「男子們正在審閱一些文件」，故為正確答案。男子皆穿著西裝，並非便服（casual clothes），因此 (C) 並非答案。

字彙 review 審閱　casual clothes 便服

2

(A) They are repairing the computer.
(B) A man is staring at the monitor.
(C) A woman is searching for a file on the computer.
(D) They are working on the computer.

(A) 他們正在修理電腦。
(B) **一名男子正盯著螢幕看。**
(C) 一名女子正在電腦裡搜尋一份檔案。
(D) 他們正在用電腦工作。

解析

男子正在看著電腦，女子站在後方看著他。(B) 描寫「男子正盯著螢幕看」，故為正確答案。請注意，因為只有男子一個人在用電腦，故千萬不要因為聽到「working on the computer」（正在用電腦工作），就誤選 (D) 作為答案。

字彙 stare at 盯著……看
　　　 search for 搜索、尋找

3

(A) The men are working in the warehouse.
(B) They are stacking up the boxes.
(C) They are unpacking the packages.
(D) One of the men is opening a box.

(A) 這些男子正在倉庫裡工作。
(B) 他們正把箱子疊起來。
(C) 他們正在拆開包裹。
(D) 其中一名男子正打開一個箱子。

解析

照片中有一名男子正在疊放箱子，另外兩名男子則在後方談話。(A) 描寫「這些男子正在倉庫工作」，為最適當的描述。請注意，因為只有一名男子在疊箱子，故千萬不要因為聽到「stacking up the boxes」（正把箱子疊起來），就誤選 (B) 作為答案。

字彙 warehouse 倉庫　stack up 把……疊起來
　　　 unpack 拆開（包裹）、打開（行李箱）

4

(A) The people are cleaning a garage.
(B) One of the people is sweeping the floor.
(C) Both of them are wearing aprons.
(D) The man is moving the chairs.

(A) 人們正在打掃車庫。
(B) 其中一人正在掃地。
(C) **他們兩人都穿著圍裙。**
(D) 男子正在搬椅子。

解析

照片中的男子和女子正在整理房間。兩人皆穿著圍裙，因此答案選 (C)。女子是用吸塵器吸地板，並非掃地（is sweeping the floor），請注意不要誤選 (B) 作為答案。

字彙 garage 車庫　sweep 清掃　apron 圍裙

03 描述事物的照片 p.18

STEP 1 題型演練

> 1 (O) 2 (O) 3 (X) 4 (X) 5 (X)
> 6 (X) 7 (X)

1 花留在桌上。
2 房間的燈打開了。
3 桌上放著茶點。
4 （某人）正在將花插進花瓶中。
5 沙發面向時鐘。
6 工人正在用吸塵器吸地毯。
7 （某人）正在上茶點。

STEP 3 聽寫練習

> 1 (C) (D)   2 (B)

1

(A) A laptop is being used.
(B) Some books are piled on the floor.
(C) A potted plant has been placed on the table.
(D) Glasses are positioned next to a cell phone.

(A) （某人）正在使用筆電。
(B) 一些書堆放在地板上。
(C) 桌上放著一盆盆栽。
(D) 眼鏡放在手機旁邊。

解析

確認完照片中事物的位置後，請仔細聆聽選項中的介系詞，並選出正確答案。桌上放著一個盆栽，且眼鏡放在手機旁邊，所以答案選 (C) 和 (D)。照片中沒有人使用筆電，因此 (A) 並非答案；書放在桌上而不是地上，所以也不能選 (B)。

字彙 pile 堆疊 potted plant 盆栽

2

(A) Groceries have been placed in a cart.
(B) Fruit is on display in a store.
(C) A customer is weighing some fruit on a scale.
(D) Some food is being put into a basket.

(A) 手推車裡放著食品雜貨。
(B) 商店裡陳列著水果。
(C) 一名顧客正用磅秤稱一些水果。
(D) （某人）正把一些食物放進籃子裡。

解析

食品雜貨並未放在手推車內，因此 (A) 並非答案；照片中並未出現人物，因此 (C) 和 (D) 也不是答案；(B) 描寫水果陳列的狀態，故為正確答案。

字彙 grocery 食品雜貨 customer 顧客
     scale 磅秤

實戰演練 p.20

> 1 (B) 2 (A) 3 (B) 4 (D)

1

(A) There are trees in the park.
(B) A picnic basket has been left on the grass.
(C) A gardener is mowing the grass.
(D) Dishes are being served.

6

(A) 公園裡有樹。
(B) 草地上留有一個野餐籃。
(C) 園丁正在除草。
(D) （某人）正在上菜。

解析

照片中並未出現樹和除草的人，因此 (A) 和 (C) 並非答案；照片中沒有看到上菜的人，因此 (D) 也不是答案；(B) 描寫籃子放在草地上的狀態，故為正確答案。

字彙 gardener 園丁　mow 除（草坪等上面）的草

2

(A) **Kitchen pots are positioned on the stove.**
(B) Vegetables are being washed.
(C) Dishes have been stacked on the countertop.
(D) There is a knife on the chopping board.

(A) 爐子上放著廚房的鍋子。
(B) （某人）正在洗蔬菜。
(C) 盤子堆放在廚房料理檯上。
(D) 砧板上有一把刀。

解析

(A) 描寫鍋子擺放的狀態，故為正確答案。照片中並未出現盤子，因此 (C) 並非答案；照片中沒有出現洗菜的人，因此 (B) 也不是答案。

字彙 countertop （廚房）料理檯的檯面
chopping board 砧板

3

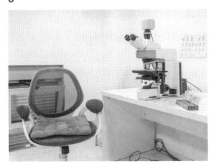

(A) Office equipment is being moved.
(B) A microscope has been placed on the table.
(C) A round table has been set up in the room.
(D) Lights have been installed on the ceiling.

(A) （某人）正在搬動辦公室設備。
(B) 桌子上放著一台顯微鏡。
(C) 房間裡擺放著一張圓桌。
(D) 天花板上安裝著燈具。

解析

描寫事物的狀態時，可使用現在完成式被動語態（have/has + been + p.p.）。(B) 便是使用現在完成式被動語態，描寫顯微鏡放置於桌上，故為正確答案。

字彙 office equipment 辦公室設備　install 安裝
ceiling 天花板

4

(A) There are customers at a cash register.
(B) Products are being arranged on the shelves.
(C) A clerk is stocking the shelves with cans.
(D) A shopping cart has been filled with groceries.

(A) 收銀機前有一些顧客。
(B) （某人）正把商品排到貨架上。
(C) 一名店員正把罐頭補滿貨架。
(D) 一台購物車裡裝滿了食品雜貨。

解析

(D) 使用現在完成式被動語態，描寫購物車內裝滿食品雜貨的狀態。照片中並未出現人物，因此 (A) 和 (C) 並非答案；若聽到事物主詞後方使用現在進行式被動語態（is/are + being + p.p.），該句話描述的通常是人物的動作，適用於人物照片，因此 (B) 也不是答案。

字彙 cash register 收銀機　arrange 排列
　　　 stock 為……備貨、把……填滿

04 描述背景的照片
p.22

STEP 1 題型演練

| 1 (O) | 2 (O) | 3 (X) | 4 (X) | 5 (O) |
| 6 (X) | 7 (X) | | | |

1 雪覆蓋了地面。
2 靠近房子的地方種了一些樹。
3 （某人）正在打掃房子。
4 雪已經清乾淨了。
5 這兩棟房子中間有一些樹。
6 所有的窗戶都開著。
7 （某人）正在擦窗戶。

STEP 3 聽寫練習

| 1 (A) (D) | 2 (B) (C) |

1

(A) A boat is docked in a harbor.
(B) There is a boat sailing in the water.
(C) The boat is ready to sail.
(D) There is a bridge over the water.

(A) 一艘船停在港口。
(B) 有艘船在水中航行。
(C) 這艘船準備好要出航。
(D) 水面上有一座橋。

解析

照片中有一艘船停靠於港口，水上有一座橋，因此答案為 (A) 和 (D)。光看照片並無法判斷船隻是否在航行、船隻是否準備出航，因此 (B) 和 (C) 並非答案。

字彙 dock（使）停泊、（使）進港
　　 sail（船）航行

2

(A) Some cars have been parked in the driveway.
(B) There is a lawn near the house.
(C) There is a car in front of the house.
(D) The road is shaded by the house.

(A) 有些車停在車道上。
(B) 靠近房子處有一片草坪。
(C) 房子前面有一輛車。
(D) 這條路被房子擋住了陽光。

解析

照片裡可以看到房子前方有草坪，還停了一輛車，因此答案選 (B) 和 (C)。

字彙 driveway 車道　lawn 草坪

實戰演練
p.24

| 1 (B) | 2 (B) | 3 (A) | 4 (C) |

1

(A) Cars are stopped at the traffic light.
(B) Vehicles are traveling in both directions.
(C) The buildings are under construction.
(D) Some cars are being checked.

(A) 車子停在紅綠燈前面。
(B) 雙向都有車子在行駛。
(C) 大樓正在興建中。
(D) 有些車子正在接受檢查。

解析

照片中的車子往兩個不同的方向移動，因此答案為 (B)。請特別留意動詞 traveling 可以用來表示車輛正在移動。(C) 故意使用 building（大樓），為陷阱選項；車子並未停在紅綠燈前、也沒有人在檢查車子（being checked），因此 (A) 和 (D) 皆不是答案。

字彙 traffic light 紅綠燈
under construction 興建中

2

(A) The trees are being watered.
(B) A path runs through the woods.
(C) A hiking trail has been blocked.
(D) The road is being paved.

(A)（某人）正在給樹木澆水。
(B) 一條小路穿過樹林。
(C) 一條健行步道封閉了。
(D)（某人）正在鋪設路面。

解析

(B) 使用「run through the woods」（穿過樹林），正確描寫照片中的林間步道，故為正確答案。(A) 和 (D) 都使用現在進行式被動語態，但照片中未出現人物，與情景不相符；健行步道並未被封閉（has been blocked），因此 (C) 也不是答案。

字彙 block 堵住、封鎖　pave 鋪、築（路面）

3

(A) There are shelves hanging on the wall.
(B) The garage is being cleaned.
(C) The tires are being put away.
(D) There is some equipment scattered on the floor.

(A) 牆上懸掛著一些架子。
(B)（某人）正在打掃車庫。
(C)（某人）正在把輪胎收好。
(D) 地板上散落著一些用具。

解析

倉庫內的牆上掛著架子，(A) 使用「hanging on the wall」（牆上懸掛著……）描寫，故為正確答案。照片中並未出現人物，因此 (B) 和 (C) 皆不是答案；用具並未散落在地上，因此 (D) 也不是答案。

字彙 hang 懸掛　put away 把……收好
scatter 散布

4

(A) The bird is flying in the sky.
(B) Some people are waiting to get food.
(C) A statue is overlooking the square.
(D) The gate is wide open.

(A) 鳥正在空中飛。
(B) 有些人正在等著領取食物。
(C) 一座雕像俯瞰著廣場。
(D) 大門敞開著。

解析

(C) 使用「overlook the square」（俯瞰著廣場），描寫廣場上放置了一座大型雕像，故為正確答案。

字彙 statue 雕像　overlook 俯瞰　square 廣場

A

1 (A) 2 (B) 3 (B) 4 (A) 5 (B)

B

| 1 towed | 2 reviewing | 3 planted |
| 4 stacked | 5 displayed | |

C

1 is watering potted plants
2 is taking a coat off / is taking off a coat
3 is trying on a necklace / is trying a necklace on
4 have been parked along
5 is reaching for a cell phone

PART 2 | 應答問題 Questions & Responses

01 WH 問句（1）who, what   p.28

Who

STEP 1 題型演練

1 (A) 2 (B) 3 (B) 4 (A) 5 (A)

1

誰是新任的業務經理？
(A) 莎拉・貝克。
(B) 我沒有看到。

2

你僱用誰來整修辦公室？
(A) 代理商。
(B) 甲蟲營造。

3

誰負責預算會議？
(A) 下午。
(B) 業務部主管。

4

我應該找誰談員工訓練的事？
(A) 人事部。
(B) 下週。

5

誰有預算案的報告？
(A) 我想莎拉有。
(B) 在櫃子裡。

STEP 3 聽寫練習

| 1 (B) (C) | 2 (A) (B) | 3 (A) |
| 4 (B) | 5 (A) (C) | 6 (C) |

1

Who is in charge of the Peterson project?
(A) The projector is not working.
(B) Ask the supervisor.
(C) Tim in the Sales Department.

誰負責彼德森專案？
(A) 投影機故障了。
(B) 問一下主管。
(C) 業務部的提姆。

解析

請務必聽清楚疑問詞。本題為 who 開頭的問句，詢問「是誰」。(C) 具體回答出人名，故為正確答案；(B) 採間接回答的方式，同樣可以作為答案。

字彙 in charge of 負責……

2

Who should I talk to about the training session?
(A) The Personnel Department.
(B) Ms. Kim might know.
(C) Yes, you can talk to me.

我要找誰談訓練講習的事？
(A) 人事部。
(B) 金女士可能知道。
(C) 是的，你可以和我談。

解析

題目為 who 開頭的問句時，除了回答人名之外，也可以回答職稱或部門名稱。因此在本題當中，除了回答人名的 (B) 之外，回答部門名稱的 (A) 也可以作為答案。

3

Who is the head of the Accounting Department?
(A) It's Ms. Rylan.
(B) No, I don't have it.
(C) The evaluations have been finished.

會計部的主管是誰？
(A) 是瑞蘭女士。
(B) 不，我沒有。
(C) 估價已完成。

解析
(A) 直接使用人名回答 who 開頭的問句，故為正確答案。

4

Who did you meet at the annual conference?
(A) I am the organizer.
(B) Employees at our competitors.
(C) He is not the right person.

你在年會時遇到誰？
(A) 我是籌辦者。
(B) 我們競爭對手的員工。
(C) 他不是合適的人。

解析
本題詢問跟誰見面，(B) 回答見了競爭對手的員工，故為正確答案。雖然 (A) 和 (C) 都有提到人，但是內容皆不符合題意。

字彙 annual 每年的　organizer 組織者、籌辦者

5

Who is going to give a speech at the seminar?
(A) I think Ann is.
(B) He was such an excellent speaker.
(C) It has not been decided yet.

誰將要在研討會上發表演說？
(A) 我想是安。
(B) 他是一位非常出色的講者。
(C) 還沒有決定。

解析
(A) 提到人名，故為正確答案；(C) 表示還沒決定，也是適當的回答方式。

字彙 give a speech 發表演說

6

Who is writing the budget proposal?
(A) We're sending it tomorrow.
(B) On the second floor.
(C) I'll check and let you know.

誰正在寫預算案？
(A) 我們明天會送出去。
(B) 在二樓。
(C) 我會查一下，然後跟你說。

解析
(C) 表示確認過後再告訴對方，屬於間接回答的方式。這類選項通常都是正確答案。本題中詢問的是撰寫預算案的人，(C) 的回答方式同樣適用。

字彙 budget 預算　proposal 提案、計畫書

What

STEP 1 題型演練

| 1 (A) | 2 (B) | 3 (B) | 4 (A) | 5 (A) |

1

行銷部要求什麼東西？
(A) 去年的銷售記錄。
(B) 他們有很多問題。

2

和韓先生聯絡最好的方式是什麼？
(A) 你可以告訴我他的聯絡資訊。
(B) 也許打他的手機。

3

你覺得調查結果如何？
(A) 他們現在應該離開。
(B) 結果令人滿意。

4

我幾點可以登記入住飯店？
(A) 3 點之後都可以。
(B) 應該要打掃。

5

我們的新建築師叫什麼名字？
(A) 我想是卡蘿‧史密斯。
(B) 那是家優良的公司。

STEP 3 聽寫練習

| 1 (B) (C) | 2 (A) | 3 (C) |
| 4 (B) | 5 (B) (C) | 6 (A) (B) |

1

What is the membership fee at the yoga center?
(A) All the staff members.
(B) Thirty dollars a month.
(C) I am not really sure.

瑜珈中心的會費是多少？
(A) 所有的職員。
(B) 一個月 30 美元。
(C) 我不太確定。

解析

雖然本題為 what 開頭的問句，但實際上詢問的是價格。(B) 回答正確的資訊，故為正確答案；(C) 表示自己不太清楚，同樣可以作為答案。

字彙 fee 費用（如學費、會費、入場費等）

2

What do you think of the floor plan?
(A) It's a great design.
(B) He is an excellent architect.
(C) It needs to be cleaned.

你覺得樓層平面圖如何？
(A) 設計很棒。
(B) 他是一位傑出的建築師。
(C) 需要打掃。

解析

詢問對方的意見時，會使用句型「What do you think of/about . . . ?」。本題詢問對方對樓層平面圖的想法，(A) 持正面看法，故為正確答案。

字彙 floor plan 樓層平面圖　architect 建築師

3

What software would you recommend?
(A) Somewhere in the corner.
(B) I found it very creative.
(C) How about this one here?

你推薦哪種軟體？
(A) 在角落的某處。
(B) 我覺得很有創意。
(C) 這邊這個怎麼樣？

解析

當 what 後方連接名詞時，請務必聽清楚該名詞，才能選出正確答案。本題詢問對方推薦什麼樣的軟體，(C) 直接建議特定的產品，故為最適當的回答。

4

What floor is KT Technology on?
(A) I am working on it.
(B) There's a building directory there.
(C) They haven't delivered it yet.

KT 科技在幾樓？
(A) 我正在處理。
(B) 那裡有一張大樓住戶一覽表。
(C) 他們還沒有送。

解析

與前一題相同，請務必聽清楚 what 後方的名詞。本題詢問在幾樓，(B) 並未回答明確的樓層，而是告知對方確認的方法，為適當的回答。

5

What did the accountant ask for?
(A) No, the sales representative did.
(B) He just asked a few questions.
(C) The tax forms.

會計要求什麼東西？
(A) 不是，是業務代表做的。
(B) 他只問了幾個問題。
(C) 報稅表格。

解析

WH 問句不能以 Yes 或 No 來回答，因此 (A) 不能作為答案。(B) 表示沒有要東西，只是問了幾個問題、(C) 回答對方要求提供報稅表格，皆為適當的回答。

字彙 accountant 會計師
representative 代表、代理人

6

What time are you meeting with the lawyer?
(A) Right after lunch.
(B) At 11 o'clock.
(C) It's about the new contract.

你什麼時候要見律師？
(A) 就在午餐之後。
(B) 11 點。
(C) 是有關新合約的事。

解析

本題詢問時間，(A) 和 (B) 分別回答出明確的時間點，故為正確答案。

1 (C)	2 (B)	3 (B)	4 (A)	5 (A)
6 (C)	7 (A)	8 (C)	9 (C)	10 (A)

1

Who's the new accounting manager?
(A) This report is complicated.
(B) He is away on vacation.
(C) Someone from headquarters.

誰是新任的會計部經理？
(A) 這份報告很複雜。
(B) 他去度假不在。
(C) 從總公司派來的某個人。

解析

本題為 who 開頭的問句。雖然 (C) 並未回答確切的人名，但是提到此人為總公司的人，同樣可以作為答案。

字彙 complicated 複雜的　on vacation 在度假　headquarters 總公司

2

What time does your train come?
(A) At Central Station.
(B) In about 10 minutes.
(C) Because trains are quicker.

你的火車幾點來？
(A) 在中央車站。
(B) 大約十分鐘後。
(C) 因為火車比較快。

解析

本題詢問火車什麼時候會來，(B) 表示「十分鐘後」，為適當的回答。(B) 的 in 解釋為「在……之後」。

3

Who chose the catering service for the banquet?
(A) I chose the venue.
(B) Tom at the reception desk.
(C) The food was excellent.

宴會的外燴公司是誰選的？
(A) 地點是我選的。
(B) 接待處的湯姆。
(C) 食物非常棒。

解析

面對以 who 開頭的問句，(B) 直接回答出人名，故為正確答案。(A) 和 (C) 分別使用與題目句有關的單字 venue（地點）和 food（食物），故意使人產生混淆，但並非答案。

字彙 venue（事件、行動等的）發生地點　reception desk 接待處、飯店櫃檯

4

Who should I talk to about the company's move?
(A) The maintenance team.
(B) I asked him before.
(C) No, not in a month.

關於公司搬遷的事，我應該找誰談？
(A) 維修團隊。
(B) 我以前問過他。
(C) 不，不是一個月後。

解析

本題為 who 開頭的問句，(C) 以 No 回答，並不適當。題目詢問應該跟誰討論「公司搬遷」一事，(A) 回答部門名稱，故為正確答案。

字彙 maintenance team 維修團隊

5

What kind of desk should we order for our new office?
(A) I will keep my old one.
(B) We need more chairs.
(C) No, bigger ones.

我們應該為我們的新辦公室訂購什麼樣的辦公桌？
(A) 我要繼續用舊的桌子。
(B) 我們需要更多椅子。
(C) 不，要更大的桌子。

解析

WH 問句不能使用 Yes 或 No 來回答，因此 (C) 並非答案。(B) 故意使用與題目句中 desk（辦公桌）有關的單字 chair（椅子），是陷阱選項。(A) 表示要繼續使用舊的桌子，等於不打算訂購新辦公桌的意思，故為正確答案。

6

What took you so long to finish the budget report?
(A) It is quite tight this year.
(B) Alan helped me.
(C) I had a meeting to attend.

你怎麼花這麼久時間才完成預算報告？
(A) 今年相當吃緊。
(B) 亞倫幫我的。
(C) 我有一個會議要參加。

解析

「What took you so long . . . ?」問的是「為什麼會花這麼久時間」。(C) 表示有個必須參加的會議，明確交代原因，為最適當的回答。

字彙 budget 預算　quite 相當、很
　　　　tight（時間、金錢）緊的、拮据的

7

Who is in charge of organizing the workshop?
(A) I believe Emily is.
(B) It was informational.
(C) It's not far from here.

誰負責籌備工作坊？
(A) 我想是艾蜜莉。
(B) 有資訊性的。
(C) 離這裡不遠。

解析

(A) 以人名回答 who 開頭的問句，故為正確答案。其餘選項皆答非所問。

字彙 in charge of 負責……
　　　　informational 有資訊性的

8

What did you think of the parade yesterday?
(A) Are you available?
(B) Yes, it's on Sunday.
(C) It was too crowded.

你覺得昨天的遊行如何？
(A) 你有空嗎？
(B) 是的，是在週日。
(C) 太擁擠了。

解析

「What do you think of . . . ? / what did you think of . . . ?」用於詢問對方的意見。本題詢問對方對遊行的看法，(C) 表示非常擁擠，為適當的回答。

字彙 crowded 擁擠的

9

Who reviewed the applications?
(A) That sounds like a plan.
(B) About 5 million dollars.
(C) The general manager did.

是誰審閱申請表的？
(A) 那聽起來不錯。
(B) 大約 500 萬美元。
(C) 是總經理。

解析

本題為 who 開頭的問句，(C) 回答職稱，為最適當的回答。其餘選項皆不適合用來回答 who 開頭的問句。

字彙 review 審閱　application 申請表
　　　　sound like a plan = sound good 聽起來不錯

10

What do you think of the new work shifts?
(A) I can't complain.
(B) Ms. Cooper did.
(C) Yes, I work at night.

你覺得新的班表如何？
(A) 我沒有什麼好抱怨的地方。
(B) 庫柏女士排的。
(C) 是的，我上晚班。

解析

本題詢問對方的意見，(A) 表示沒有什麼好抱怨的地方，等同於滿意，故為正確答案。(B) 回答人名，答非所問；(C) 回答 Yes，並不適合用來回答 WH 問句。

字彙 work shift 輪班工作的時段
　　　　complain 抱怨、投訴

02 WH 問句（2）which, when　　　p.34

Which

STEP 1 題型演練

1 (A)　2 (B)　3 (B)　4 (B)　5 (A)

1

你在修哪一門課？
(A) 有關醫療保健的那一門。
(B) 他們沒有開那門課。

2

你現在訂哪一家報紙？
(A) 我不喜歡閱讀。
(B) 你昨天建議的那一家。

3

他要去哪一個部門？
(A) 我覺得不是那樣。
(B) 我猜是業務部。

4

你想買哪一個，大的還是小的？
(A) 恐怕是這樣。
(B) 哪一個都可以。

5

銀行在哪條街上？
(A) 你最好問卡蘿。
(B) 我不需要領錢。

1 (B) (C)	2 (A) (C)	3 (C)
4 (A)	5 (B)	6 (A)

1

Which bag belongs to Mr. Evans?
(A) I don't belong here.
(B) The one with the red tag.
(C) The one in the corner.

哪個是伊凡斯先生的包包？
(A) 我不是本地人。
(B) 有紅色標籤那個。
(C) 在角落那個。

解析

本題詢問「哪個是 Mr. Evans（伊凡斯先生）的包包」。(B) 表示為有紅色標籤的包包、(C) 表示為放在角落的那個包包，皆為正確答案。動詞 belong 的意思為「屬於……」，但此處的意思為「屬於這裡」＝「本地人」，千萬不要因為聽到這個單字，就誤選 (A) 作為答案。

字彙 **belong to** 屬於……

2

Which of the books should I buy?
(A) Neither. I can loan you both.
(B) The bookstore is right around the corner.
(C) Either is fine.

我應該買哪本書？
(A) 都別買。這兩本我都可以借你。
(B) 書店就在附近。
(C) 哪一本都可以。

解析

本題詢問「應該買哪本書」。(A) 表示兩本都不用，自己願意出借、(C) 表示不管買哪一本都行，兩者皆為正確答案。either 的意思為「兩者當中擇一」，適合用來回答選擇性疑問句，表示無論選擇哪個都可以。

字彙 **loan** 借出、貸款　**around the corner** 在附近

3

Which of the teams is in charge of payroll?
(A) It is being processed.
(B) The team played so well.
(C) Ms. Rolling's team, I guess.

哪個團隊負責發薪水？
(A) 正在處理中。
(B) 那個團隊表現得非常好。
(C) 我想是羅琳女士的團隊。

解析

本題詢問「哪個團隊負責發薪水」，(C) 表示為 Ms. Rolling（羅琳女士）的團隊，故為正確答案。

字彙 **payroll** 發薪名單

4

Which of you is interested in the workshop?
(A) Jeremy looks more interested.
(B) It was so helpful.
(C) It turned out so well.

你們哪一個人對那個工作坊有興趣？
(A) 傑瑞米看起來比較感興趣。
(B) 非常有幫助。
(C) 結果很好。

解析

本題詢問「哪一個人對工作坊有興趣」，(A) 表示 Jeremy（傑瑞米）比較感興趣，故為正確答案。

字彙 **turn out** 結果是……（尤指出乎意料的結果）

5

Which of the restaurants do you want me to reserve a table at?
(A) The restaurant is closed.
(B) The one on Denver Street.
(C) I forgot to make a reservation.

你想要我訂哪一家餐廳？
(A) 餐廳打烊了。
(B) 丹佛街那一家。
(C) 我忘記訂位了。

PART

2

02 WH 問句 (2) which, when

本題詢問「想訂哪一家餐廳」,(B) 表示位於 Denver Street(丹佛街)上的餐廳,故為正確答案。此處使用代名詞「the one」來代替餐廳。

字彙 reserve 預約、預訂
make a reservation 預約、預訂

6

Which candidate do you think is more qualified?
(A) The guy with more experience.
(B) I don't have any qualifications.
(C) It's been discussed.

你認為哪一位應徵者更能勝任?
(A) 經驗較豐富的那位。
(B) 我沒有任何資格。
(C) 已經討論過了。

解析

本題詢問「哪一位應徵者更能勝任」,(A) 表示經驗較為豐富者,故為適當的回答。值得留意的是 qualifications 的意思為「資格條件」,千萬不要因為聽到該單字,就誤選 (B) 作為答案。

字彙 candidate 候選人、應徵者
qualified 有資格的、勝任的
qualification 資格條件

When

STEP 1 題型演練

1 (B)　2 (A)　3 (B)　4 (B)　5 (A)

1

你何時搬來這棟大樓的?
(A) 上一個。
(B) 大約六個月前。

2

你打算何時離開這家公司?
(A) 我必須先跟我的主管談談。
(B) 我住在離這裡不遠的地方。

3

我們何時要討論合約的細節?
(A) 沒那麼簡單。
(B) 你何時方便?

4

包裹何時會遞送?
(A) 我還沒有訂購。
(B) 下週的某一天。

5

我們何時要寫完報告?
(A) 最晚下週一。
(B) 至少我們必須做。

STEP 3 聽寫練習

1 (A) (C)　　2 (B)　　3 (A) (B)
4 (A) (B)　　5 (B) (C)　　6 (A)

1

When do we have to have our next company banquet?
(A) We'd better check with the manager.
(B) Last year's party was terrific.
(C) We haven't decided yet.

公司下一次的宴會須辦在何時?
(A) 我們最好和經理確認一下。
(B) 去年的派對棒極了。
(C) 我們還沒有決定。

解析

本題詢問「公司宴會辦在何時」。(A) 表示得跟經理確認、(C) 表示目前還沒決定,兩個回答皆符合題意。

字彙 banquet(正式的)宴會　terrific 極好的

2

When did you come back from your business trip?
(A) Next Friday.
(B) Yesterday.
(C) I am still working on it.

你何時出差回來的?
(A) 下週五。
(B) 昨天。
(C) 我還在處理。

解析

本題詢問「何時出差回來的」,(B) 回答時間為昨天,故為正確答案。請特別注意,千萬不要因為聽到問句使用疑問詞 when,便直接選擇 (A) Next Friday 作為答案。

3

When will the renovations be finished?

(A) It's hard to say.

(B) By the end of the month.

(C) The innovation was successful.

整修工程何時會完工？

(A) 很難說。

(B) 月底之前。

(C) 創新很成功。

解析

本題詢問「整修工程何時完工」。(A) 表示這很難說、(B) 表示在月底之前，皆為正確答案。而這類考題的答案通常為 (A) 這種不明確的回答。(C) 故意使用 innovation（創新），跟題目中的 renovation（整修）發音相近，屬於陷阱選項。

字彙 renovation 整修　innovation 創新

4

When is the deadline for the project?

(A) It has been postponed until next month.

(B) I am not quite sure.

(C) I am working around the clock.

這個專案的截止期限是何時？

(A) 已經延到下個月了。

(B) 我不太確定。

(C) 我正日以繼夜地工作。

解析

本題詢問「專案的截止期限」。(A) 表示延到下個月，為適當的答案。另外，如同前一題，(B) 表示「不太確定」，屬於不明確的回答，也是適當的答案。

5

When are we supposed to meet our clients?

(A) The meeting was good.

(B) That hasn't been decided yet.

(C) The day after tomorrow.

我們應該何時和客戶見面？

(A) 會面很愉快。

(B) 還沒有決定。

(C) 後天。

解析

本題詢問「何時與客戶見面」。(B) 表示還沒決定、(C) 表示「後天」，皆為正確答案。當中選項 (B) 仍是以不明確的回答作為答案。

字彙 be supposed to（被認為）應該……
client 客戶

6

When should I remind you to leave?

(A) 30 minutes from now.

(B) This is a reminder.

(C) I hope so.

我應該何時提醒你該走了？

(A) 30 分鐘之後。

(B) 這是一則提醒。

(C) 希望是這樣。

解析

本題詢問「應該何時提醒你該走」。(A) 表示從現在算起 30 分鐘後，故為正確答案。(B) reminder 為名詞，意思為「提醒者／物」。

字彙 remind 提醒　reminder 提醒者／物

實戰演練　　　　　　　　p.38

1 (B)	2 (A)	3 (A)	4 (B)	5 (C)
6 (A)	7 (B)	8 (C)	9 (A)	10 (A)

1

Which of the computers do you want me to purchase?

(A) The sooner, the better.

(B) The latest one.

(C) It will cost a lot of money.

你想要我買哪一款電腦？

(A) 愈快愈好。

(B) 最新款的。

(C) 要花很多錢。

解析

本題詢問「要買哪一款電腦」，(B) 表示要最新款的，故為正確答案。

2

When will the consultants arrive in Seoul?

(A) At the end of the week.

(B) They will help us a lot.

(C) Seoul is an attractive place.

顧問何時會抵達首爾？

(A) 這個週末。

(B) 他們會幫我們很多忙。

(C) 首爾是個漂亮迷人的地方。

解析

本題詢問「顧問何時會抵達 Seoul（首爾）」，(A) 表示這個週末，故為正確答案。其他兩個選項的回答皆與「時間」無關。

字彙 **attractive** 漂亮迷人的、有吸引力的

3

Which highway should I take to get to the city?
(A) I am not familiar with this area.
(B) Take the subway.
(C) The traffic is awful.

我該走哪一條公路去城裡？
(A) 我對這一帶不熟。
(B) 搭地下鐵。
(C) 交通狀況很糟。

解析

本題詢問「走哪一條公路去城裡」，(A) 表示對這一帶不甚熟悉，故為正確答案。(B) 和 (C) 的回答都跟交通有關，請特別留意不要選錯。

字彙 **be familiar with** 熟悉……
awful 極糟的、可怕的

4

Which of these shirts looks good on me?
(A) Men's clothing.
(B) The blue one.
(C) He doesn't look well today.

這些襯衫中，我穿哪件好看？
(A) 男裝。
(B) 藍色那件。
(C) 他今天看起來精神不好。

解析

本題詢問「我穿哪件襯衫好看」，(B) 表示藍色那件，故為正確答案。(C)「look well」是連綴動詞 look ＋ 形容詞 well，指的是「身體、健康狀態良好」。若要形容外表好看，須用「look good」。

字彙 **look well** 看上去健康、氣色好

5

Which day suits you better, Monday or Friday?
(A) I enjoyed both of them.
(B) Today is Monday.
(C) The latter is better for me.

你哪一天比較方便，週一還是週五？
(A) 我兩個都喜歡。
(B) 今天是週一。
(C) 後者比較好。

解析

本題詢問「週一和週五哪一天比較好」，要求對方做出「選擇」。(C) 表示後者（the latter）為佳，即週五比較方便，故為正確答案。「後者」的相反詞為「the former」，意思為「前者」。注意 (A) 為過去式，故不能作為答案。

字彙 **suit** 對……方便、適合

6

When is the quarterly report going to be ready?
(A) We are proofreading it now.
(B) We didn't do well last quarter.
(C) It has been rejected.

季報告何時會好？
(A) 我們現在正在校對。
(B) 我們上一季表現不好。
(C) 被退回來了。

解析

本題詢問「季報告何時會好」，(A) 表示「正在校對」，故為正確答案。(B) 故意使用單字 quarter（季），與題目中的 quarterly（季的）發音相近，意圖使人產生混淆。

字彙 **proofread** 校對　　**quarter** 季

7

When are you going to leave for the sales conference?
(A) It seems like a long time ago.
(B) After work today.
(C) The sales manager will be there.

你什麼時候要去開銷售會議？
(A) 好像是很久以前的事了。
(B) 今天下班後。
(C) 業務經理會在場。

解析

本題詢問「打算何時去開銷售會議」，(B) 表示今天下班後，故為正確答案。(A) 意指過去的事、(C) 提到參加者，皆答非所問。

8

Which of these products are made locally?
(A) I got it.
(B) They aren't produced anymore.
(C) Neither of them.

這些產品裡，哪一個是在當地製造的？
(A) 我懂了。
(B) 不再生產了。
(C) 兩個都不是。

解析

本題詢問「哪個產品是在當地製造的」，(C) 表示兩者皆非，故為正確答案。選擇性疑問句的答案經常採用此種回答方式。

字彙 locally 在當地

9

Which department are you working in, Accounting or Finance?
(A) I am in Sales.
(B) Accountants will be here.
(C) I haven't been there.

你在哪個部門工作，會計部還是財務部？
(A) 我在業務部。
(B) 會計會來這裡。
(C) 我沒去過那裡。

解析

本題詢問「任職於會計部還是財務部」，(A) 回答的是「業務部」，故為正確答案。題目為選擇性疑問句時，可以跳脫問題中的兩個選項，回答第三種選項作為答案。

10

When do you think I can get my car back?
(A) It's hard to tell.
(B) It has been sold already.
(C) Last Friday.

你覺得我何時能把車子取回來？
(A) 很難說。
(B) 已經賣掉了。
(C) 上週五。

解析

本題詢問「何時能把車子取回來」，(A) 表示很難說，故為正確答案。請特別留意「I'm not sure.」或「It's hard to tell.」這類較為婉轉的回答方式，同樣可以作為答案。

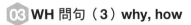

03 WH 問句（3）why, how p.40

p.40

Why

STEP 1 題型演練

| 1 (A) | 2 (B) | 3 (A) | 4 (B) | 5 (B) |

1
您為什麼想退錢？
(A) 這個商品有損壞。
(B) 打 95 折。

2
你為什麼打電話給倉庫經理？
(A) 我們有很多。
(B) 為了詢問存貨。

3
我們何不現在看看調查的結果？
(A) 好啊，我有時間。
(B) 是的，那很好。

4
82 號公路為什麼封閉了？
(A) 我們可以開車去。
(B) 因為在施工。

5
山緲今天為什麼沒上班？
(A) 在二樓。
(B) 他今天要去做健康檢查。

STEP 3 聽寫練習

| 1 (A) (C) | 2 (B) (C) | 3 (A) |
| 4 (A) | 5 (A) (B) | 6 (B) (C) |

1
Why is your furniture covered in plastic?
(A) There's a water leak in the ceiling.
(B) He will recover soon.
(C) We are moving to a new house.

你的家具為什麼蓋著塑膠布？
(A) 天花板漏水。
(B) 他很快就會康復。
(C) 我們正要搬到新家。

解析

本題詢問把塑膠製品覆蓋在家具上的原因。(A) 表示因為天花板漏水、(C) 表示因為即將要搬家,皆為適當的答覆。(B) 故意使用 recover（康復）,與 cover（覆蓋）的發音相近,意圖使人產生混淆。

字彙 **leak**（液體或氣體）漏出　**ceiling** 天花板
recover 康復

2

Why don't we put off the sales meeting?
(A) It's on the third floor.
(B) Okay. Let's reschedule it.
(C) How about this Friday then?

我們何不將業務會議延期?
(A) 在三樓。
(B) 好,我們重新安排會議時間吧。
(C) 那麼這週五怎麼樣?

解析

本題使用問句建議將會議延期。(B) 表示同意調整時間、(C) 提議延到其他天,皆為適當的答覆。(A) 提及開會地點,答非所問。

字彙 **put off** 延後
reschedule 重新安排……的時間

3

Why did the Accounting Department send this memo?
(A) I haven't checked it yet.
(B) I'm sure they did.
(C) The figures are wrong.

會計部為什麼送這份備忘錄來?
(A) 我還沒確認。
(B) 我確定他們做了。
(C) 數字是錯的。

解析

本題詢問會計部門送來備忘錄的原因。(A) 表示還沒進行確認,故為正確答案。(B) 重複使用 did、(C) 故意提到單字 figure（數字）,與「Accounting Department」（會計部）有關,意圖使人產生混淆。

字彙 **figure** 數字、金額

4

Why don't you attend the international conference?
(A) Let me think about it.
(B) By airplane.
(C) Room 201 is available.

你何不參加國際會議?
(A) 讓我考慮一下。
(B) 搭飛機。
(C) 可以用 201 號室。

解析

本題使用句型「Why don't you . . . ?」,提議參加國際會議。(A) 表示要考慮一下,為適當的答覆。(B) 故意使用 airplane（飛機）,與題目中的 international（國際的）有關,屬於陷阱選項。

5

Why don't you sign up for the contest?
(A) I'm considering it.
(B) That's a good idea.
(C) Because of the soccer game.

你何不報名參加比賽?
(A) 我正在考慮。
(B) 那是個好主意。
(C) 因為足球比賽。

解析

本題提議報名參加比賽。(A) 和 (B) 皆採正面答覆的方式,故為正確答案。本題並非詢問原因,因此 (C) 並不正確。

字彙 **sign up for** 報名參加
consider 考慮

6

Why do we need a laptop for the meeting?
(A) I don't have one.
(B) I haven't heard that.
(C) I think we will try our new website.

我們為什麼需要帶筆電參加會議?
(A) 我沒有筆電。
(B) 我沒聽說此事。
(C) 我想（是因為）我們要測試我們的新網站。

解析

本題詢問需要筆電的原因。(B) 表示沒聽說這件事、(C) 解釋其原因,皆為正確答案。

How

STEP 1 題型演練

1 (B)　2 (A)　3 (A)　4 (B)　5 (B)

20

1

我要如何提交申請表？

(A) 週二。

(B) 用郵寄的。

2

我該如何去機場？

(A) 你可以在這裡搭特快車。

(B) 用電話。

3

你多久去一次健身中心？

(A) 一週兩次。

(B) 開車。

4

訂了幾張椅子？

(A) 在家具店。

(B) （只有）幾張吧，我想。

5

你是怎麼知道這個職缺的？

(A) 大約一週前。

(B) 我在報紙上看到的。

STEP 3 聽寫練習

1 (C)	2 (A) (B)	3 (A) (B)
4 (B)	5 (C)	6 (A)

1

How often do you back up your computer files?

(A) Very soon.

(B) Call a technician.

(C) I hardly ever do it.

你多久備份一次你的電腦檔案？

(A) 很快。

(B) 打電話找技術人員。

(C) 我幾乎不備份。

解析

「How often . . . ?」為詢問頻率的問句，本題詢問備份檔案的頻率。(C) 表示幾乎沒有在備份，故為正確答案。(A) 用來回答 when 開頭的問句。

字彙 technician 技術人員　hardly 幾乎不……

2

How far is it to the post office from here?

(A) It's about a ten-minute walk.

(B) I don't have any idea.

(C) Twice a day.

從這裡到郵局有多遠？

(A) 走路大約十分鐘。

(B) 我不知道。

(C) 一天兩次。

解析

本題詢問距離多遠。(A) 表示走路大約十分鐘、(B) 採間接回答的方式，皆為正確答案。

3

How long have you been working for IKM Technology?

(A) For about five years.

(B) Almost a year.

(C) By taxi.

你在 IKM 科技工作多久了？

(A) 大約五年了。

(B) 差不多一年。

(C) 搭計程車。

解析

本題詢問任職多久，(A) 和 (B) 回答時間，皆為正確答案。

4

How should I send the proposal for the new construction project?

(A) I will finish it by tomorrow.

(B) By express mail.

(C) The road is blocked now.

我該用什麼方式把新建案的計畫書寄出去？

(A) 我最晚明天會完成。

(B) 用快捷郵件。

(C) 那條路現在封鎖了。

解析

本題詢問方法。(B) 回答「By express mail」，表示「by＋方式」，故為正確答案。

字彙 construction 建造、施工
express mail 快捷郵件

5

How did you get the discount coupon?
(A) Yes, it's a good deal.
(B) Usually ten percent off.
(C) I printed it online.

你怎麼拿到折價券的？
(A) 是的，買得很便宜。
(B) 通常是打九折。
(C) 我從網路上印下來的。

解析

本題詢問取得折價券的方法。(C) 表示從網路上印下來的，為適當的答覆。(A) 不能使用 Yes 或 No 來回答 WH 問句，因此該選項並非答案；(B) 提到優惠比例，並不適合作為答案。

字彙 deal 交易

6

How much did you pay for the new laser printer?
(A) I don't remember exactly.
(B) From ten to twenty.
(C) The shop near the corner.

你花多少錢買那台新的雷射印表機？
(A) 我記不得確切的金額了。
(B) 從 10 到 20。
(C) 附近的店。

解析

本題詢問價格。(A) 未回答明確的金額，但間接表示自己「記不得了」，故為正確答案。

實戰演練 p.44

1 (A)	2 (C)	3 (A)	4 (B)	5 (A)
6 (B)	7 (B)	8 (C)	9 (C)	10 (B)

1

Why did we order paper from a different supplier?
(A) The price was a lot cheaper.
(B) Through a sales representative.
(C) By Wednesday.

我們為什麼跟另一家供應商訂紙？
(A) （因為）價格便宜很多。
(B) 透過業務代表。
(C) 週三之前。

解析

本題詢問更換供應商的原因。(A) 解釋原因為「價格便宜很多」，故為正確答案。

字彙 supplier 供應商
sales representative 業務代表

2

Why don't you talk about the performance review tomorrow?
(A) It has been reviewed.
(B) It was a great concert.
(C) Sure. Tomorrow sounds good.

你明天何不談談績效評估的事情？
(A) 已經審閱過了。
(B) 那是場很棒的音樂會。
(C) 好，明天沒問題。

解析

本題用問句提出建議。(C) 給予正面回應，故為正確答案。(B) 故意使用單字 concert（音樂會），與題目中的 performance（「績效」，另一意思為「表演」）有所關聯，屬於陷阱選項。

字彙 performance review 績效評估
review 審閱

3

How long will it take to deliver these clothes?
(A) Two to three days.
(B) Yes, it's possible.
(C) Shipping and handling are not included.

運送這些衣服要花多久時間？
(A) 兩到三天。
(B) 是的，有可能。
(C) 不包含物流處理費。

解析

本題詢問配送時間。(A) 表示要花兩到三天的時間，故為正確答案。(B) 不能使用 Yes 或 No 來回答 WH 問句，因此該選項並非答案。

字彙 deliver 運送、投遞
shipping and handling 物流處理（費）

4

How far is your company from Central Station?
(A) It took me twenty minutes.
(B) It's only about 100 meters.
(C) How about a taxi?

你的公司離中央車站多遠？
(A) 花了我 20 分鐘。
(B) 大約只有 100 公尺。
(C) 搭計程車如何？

解析

本題用「how far」詢問距離。(B) 表示距離大約為 100 公尺，故為正確答案。(A) 雖然有回答出所需時間，但使用的是過去式，因此不適合作為答案。

5

<u>Why</u> is the historic hotel on Pine Street <u>closed</u>?
(A) Because it's being restored.
(B) By tomorrow morning.
(C) I enjoyed <u>my stay</u>.

派恩街上那間歷史悠久的飯店為什麼關了？
(A) 因為它正在重建。
(B) 明天早上之前。
(C) 我在那裡住得很愉快。

解析

本題使用 why 問句詢問飯店未營業的原因。(A) 解釋目前正在重建，故為正確答案。

字彙 historic 歷史悠久的、有歷史意義的
restore 重建

6

<u>How soon</u> will you <u>be finished</u> with the assignment?
(A) No, you said you would.
(B) In about twenty minutes.
(C) Eric helped me a lot.

這項工作你多久能做完？
(A) 不，你說你會做的。
(B) 大約 20 分鐘內。
(C) 艾瑞克幫了我很大的忙。

解析

「how soon」意思為「多久、多快」，本題詢問要花多久時間才能完成工作。(B) 表示「大約 20 分鐘內」，為最適當的答覆。

字彙 assignment 工作

7

<u>Why don't you</u> take the afternoon flight to Chicago?
(A) It won't <u>take long</u>.
(B) I prefer a morning flight.
(C) I leave at two o'clock.

你何不搭下午的班機去芝加哥？
(A) 不會太久。
(B) 我比較喜歡搭早上的班機。
(C) 我 2 點出發。

解析

本題用問句建議對方搭乘下午的班機。(B) 表示偏好搭乘早上的班機，故為適當的答覆。

8

Why did Mr. Tanaka <u>call this meeting</u>?
(A) I met him yesterday.
(B) By phone.
(C) Because sales are going down.

田中先生為什麼召開了這次會議？
(A) 我昨天遇到他了。
(B) 用電話。
(C) 因為業績正在下滑。

解析

本題詢問召開會議的原因。(C) 表示因為業績正在下滑（Because sales are going down），提出具體原因，故為正確答案。(B)「By phone」適合用來回答詢問方法的問句。

字彙 call a meeting 召開會議
go down 下降、減少

9

How do I <u>enter your competition</u>?
(A) Please come in.
(B) The <u>winner gets</u> a hundred dollars.
(C) You can find details on our website.

我要如何參加你們的比賽？
(A) 請進。
(B) 優勝者能獲得 100 美元。
(C) 你可以在我們的網站上找到詳細資訊。

解析

本題詢問參加比賽的方法。(C) 表示可以參考網站上的內容，故為正確答案。(B) 故意使用 winner（優勝者），與 competition（比賽）有所關聯，意圖使人產生混淆。

字彙 enter 參加、進入　competition 競爭、比賽
winner 優勝者　detail 細節

10

How do I get to the Gong Yoga Center?
(A) I exercise every day.
(B) Go straight down this road.
(C) For ten minutes.

我要怎麼去功瑜珈中心？
(A) 我每天運動。
(B) 沿著這條路直走。
(C) 走十分鐘。

解析

本題詢問前往瑜伽中心的方法。(B) 明確指出路線，故為正確答案。

字彙 go straight 直走

04 be 動詞開頭問句
p.46

現在式／過去式

STEP 1 題型演練

1 (B)　2 (A)　3 (A)　4 (A)　5 (B)

1

招聘工作已經結束了嗎？
(A) 會予以挑選。
(B) 還沒有完成。

2

您在找什麼嗎？
(A) 沒有，我只是四處看看。
(B) 是的，我會。

3

我們要審閱提案嗎？
(A) 等你有空。
(B) 不，不是。

4

你當時有能找到住的地方嗎？
(A) 有，我們設法找了一個地方。
(B) 他們幫了很大的忙。

5

高橋女士明天會來參加歡迎會嗎？
(A) 她去了。
(B) 我不確定。

STEP 3 聽寫練習

1 (A)	2 (B) (C)	3 (B)
4 (A) (C)	5 (A)	6 (B)

1

Was the training course canceled?
(A) Yes, because of financial problems.
(B) The course was about presentations.
(C) I will keep doing it.

訓練課程取消了嗎？
(A) 是的，因為有財務上的問題。
(B) 這課程是有關於簡報演講的。
(C) 我會繼續做。

解析

本題詢問訓練課程是否已取消。(A) 解釋原因為財務上的問題，故為正確答案。

字彙 cancel 取消　presentation 簡報、演講

2

Is the sales report ready for the board meeting?
(A) They will show up.
(B) I am still working on it.
(C) Yes, it is all set.

董事會上要用的銷售報告準備好了嗎？
(A) 他們會出席的。
(B) 我還在做。
(C) 是的，都好了。

解析

本題詢問是否準備好董事會上用的銷售報告。(B) 表示自己正在做、(C) 表示都已準備好，皆為正確答案。如同 (B) 選項的內容，即使未使用 Yes 或 No 來回答 Yes-No question，只要內容符合題意，仍可作為答案。

字彙 board meeting 董事會
show up 露面、出席

3

Are you free to join me for dinner tonight?
(A) I already had lunch.
(B) I am sorry. I can't.
(C) Yes, I am opposed to it.

你今晚有空和我吃飯嗎？
(A) 我已經吃過午餐了。
(B) 抱歉，沒辦法。
(C) 是的，我反對。

解析

本題詢問今晚是否有空一起吃晚餐。(B) 表示拒絕，故為正確答案。(C)「be opposed to」的意思為「反對」，用於表示反對對方的意見。

4

Is it Mr. Williams who turned in his resignation?

(A) That is what I heard.

(B) They will find a replacement.

(C) No, it was Mr. Peterson.

提出辭呈的是威廉斯先生嗎？

(A) 我聽到的是那樣。

(B) 他們會找到一位接替者。

(C) 不是，是彼得森先生。

解析

本題詢問 Mr. Williams（威廉斯先生）是否提出了辭呈。(A) 表示自己有聽說此事、(C) 表示應為 Mr. Peterson（彼得森先生）才對，皆為適當的答覆。

字彙 turn in 提出　resignation 辭呈
replacement 接替者、代替物

5

Were you able to contact the consultant?

(A) Yes, he will be here soon.

(B) No, I am not consulting anyone.

(C) People will ask about it.

你有聯絡到顧問了嗎？

(A) 是的，他很快就會到。

(B) 不，我沒有和任何人商量。

(C) 人們會問。

解析

本題詢問是否已聯絡上顧問。(A) 回答「他很快就會到」，暗示已取得聯絡，故為正確答案。(B) 和 (C) 分別使用 consulting（商量）和「ask about」（詢問），與 consultant（顧問）有所關聯，意圖使人產生混淆。

6

Is the director supposed to be at the meeting?

(A) I will be gone for a few days.

(B) I suppose so.

(C) It's supposed to be good.

總監應該要出席會議嗎？

(A) 我會離開幾天。

(B) 我想是的。

(C) 應該是好的。

解析

本題詢問總監是否應該要參加會議。(B) 表示應該要參加，故為正確答案。(C) 僅重複使用「be supposed to」（應該……），屬於陷阱選項。

字彙 be supposed to（被認為）應該……

> **be ＋ there／未來式**

STEP 1 題型演練

| 1 (A) | 2 (A) | 3 (B) | 4 (B) | 5 (A) |

1

有任何關於產品的客訴嗎？

(A) 就我所知，沒有。

(B) 停產了。

2

你要離職嗎？

(A) 我正認真地考慮這件事。

(B) 我會去申請。

3

這會是他最後的機會嗎？

(A) 會很容易的。

(B) 我想是的。

4

關於傑克退休一事，有任何計畫嗎？

(A) 他很快就要退休了。

(B) 我不清楚。

5

聚會有很多人參加嗎？

(A) 比我預期的多很多。

(B) 我才剛回來而已。

STEP 3 聽寫練習

| 1 (B) (C) | 2 (A) | 3 (A) (C) |
| 4 (B) | 5 (A) | 6 (B) |

1

Are we going to need additional supplies?

(A) The stationery store is right over there.

(B) Let me check.

(C) I don't think so.

我們需要額外添購用品嗎？

(A) 文具店就在那裡。

(B) 讓我確認一下。

(C) 我覺得不需要。

本題詢問是否需要添購用品。(B) 表示要確認一下、(C) 表示應該不需要，皆為正確答案。請特別留意，千萬不要因為聽到 supplies（用品）和「stationery store」（文具店），便誤選 (A) 作為答案。

字彙 stationery store 文具店

2

Is it going to rain this afternoon?
(A) It probably will.
(B) No one knew about it.
(C) Turn it on.

今天下午會下雨嗎？
(A) 可能會。
(B) 當時沒有人知道。
(C) 把它打開。

解析

本題詢問今天下午是否會下雨。(A) 表示「可能會」，為最適當的答覆。(B) 使用過去式，因此不適合作為答案。

字彙 turn on 打開（電器）

3

Are there any promotional events going on?
(A) I hope so.
(B) In the Publicity Department.
(C) I am afraid not.

目前有任何促銷活動正在進行嗎？
(A) 我希望有。
(B) 在公關部。
(C) 恐怕沒有。

解析

本題詢問是否有正在進行的促銷活動。(A) 表示希望有、(C) 表示恐怕沒有，皆為正確答案。「I think so.」和「I guess so.」亦為適當的答覆。

4

Is the sales manager coming to the company banquet tonight?
(A) Sales haven't been very good.
(B) I wasn't told anything about it.
(C) Yes, it's the right decision.

業務經理會來參加今天晚上公司的宴會嗎？
(A) 業績一直都不太好。
(B) 我完全沒聽說。
(C) 是的，這是正確的決定。

解析

本題詢問今晚業務經理是否會來參加公司宴會。(B) 表示自己並未聽說，故為正確答案。「be told」為 tell 的被動語態，意思是「被告知、聽到」。(A) 故意使用 sales（業務、業績），意圖使人產生混淆。

5

Will you be available for tomorrow's gathering?
(A) Sorry. I have something else to do.
(B) Nothing is available.
(C) We have gathered to talk about it.

明天的聚會你有空來嗎？
(A) 抱歉，我有其他事要做。
(B) 什麼都買不到。
(C) 我們集合起來談過那件事了。

解析

本題詢問是否來參加明天的聚會。(A) 表示拒絕，故為正確答案。(B) 重複使用 available，但是是指「物品買不到」，屬於陷阱選項；(C) 則是故意使用 gather（聚集、集合），意圖使人產生混淆。

字彙 gathering 聚會、集會　　gather 聚集、集合

6

Is Mike going to take the day off tomorrow?
(A) No, it's his day off.
(B) Yes, he said he is going to see a doctor.
(C) We are going on vacation.

麥可明天是不是要休假？
(A) 不，那是他的休假日。
(B) 是的，他說要去看醫生。
(C) 我們要去度假。

解析

本題詢問 Mike（麥可）明天是否休假。(B) 表示他要去看醫生，說明他休假的原因，故為適當的答覆。請特別留意，雖然本題屬於 Yes-No Question，但是千萬不要只聽到 No，就直接選擇 (A) 作為答案。

實戰演練　　　　　　　　　　　　　　　p.50

1 (A)	2 (A)	3 (B)	4 (C)	5 (B)
6 (B)	7 (B)	8 (A)	9 (C)	10 (C)

1

Was the weather nice when you were on vacation?
(A) Unfortunately, it rained all week.
(B) I had a great vacation.
(C) Yes, it was fruitful.

你去度假時，天氣好嗎？
(A) 很遺憾，整週都在下雨。
(B) 我過了很棒的假期。
(C) 是的，成果豐碩。

解析

本題詢問度假時的天氣如何。(A) 表示整週都在下雨，為適當的答覆。(B) 僅重複單字 vacation（假期），但答非所問。(C) fruitful 的意思為「有成效的、有成果的」，不適合用來形容假期。

字彙 fruitful 有成效的、有成果的

2

Are the consultants going to come to Seoul?
(A) Yes, they said they would.
(B) He will help us.
(C) Last week.

顧問要來首爾嗎？
(A) 是的，他們說會來。
(B) 他會幫我們。
(C) 上週。

解析

本題詢問顧問是否會來 Seoul（首爾）。(A) 表示他們說會來，故為正確答案。(B) 的內容答非所問；(C) 提到過去，不適合作為答案。

3

Was your business trip successful?
(A) I am planning one.
(B) Much more than I had expected.
(C) It doesn't matter.

你出差結果順利嗎？
(A) 我正在計劃一趟旅行。
(B) 比我預期的順利多了。
(C) 沒關係。

解析

本題詢問出差是否順利。(B) 表示比原本預期的還順利，為適當的答覆。(B) 的「much more」後方省略了 successful。

4

Is laundry service available 24 hours a day?
(A) I need to wash them.
(B) He won't be ready.
(C) Yes, you can dial 9.

洗衣服務是全天候 24 小時服務的嗎？
(A) 我需要洗它們。
(B) 他還沒準備好。
(C) 是的，您可以撥 9。

解析

本題詢問是否 24 小時都能使用洗衣服務。(C) 告知洗衣服務的使用方法，故為正確答案。(A) 故意使用 wash（洗），僅與 laundry（洗衣）有關聯而已，但並非答案；(B) 故意使用「be ready」（準備好），與 available（可用的）有所關聯，意圖使人產生混淆。

5

Are you going to accept the offer?
(A) It's so kind of you.
(B) I am still undecided.
(C) Yes, I just finished them.

你要接受這個工作邀約嗎？
(A) 你人真好。
(B) 我還沒決定。
(C) 是的，我剛完成。

解析

本題詢問是否接受工作邀約。(B) 表示還沒決定，故為正確答案。千萬不要因為聽到 Yes，便誤選 (C) 作為答案。

字彙 accept 接受　undecided 未決定的

6

Is there an admission fee for the museum?
(A) It's hard to get in.
(B) It's free.
(C) There is no one.

博物館要門票嗎？
(A) 很難進去。
(B) 是免費的。
(C) 沒有人。

解析

本題詢問博物館是否要收入場費用。(B) 表示免費入場，故為最適當的答覆。(C)「no one」指的是「沒有人」，與費用無關。

字彙 admission fee 入場費用、門票

7

Is she the one who is in charge of hiring?

(A) She is not a responsible person.

(B) I don't think so.

(C) I thought about it.

她是負責招聘的人嗎？

(A) 她不是個負責任的人。

(B) 我想不是。

(C) 我想過這件事。

解析

本題詢問是否由她負責招聘程序。(B) 表示否定，故為正確答案。「I guess not.」和「I suppose not.」亦為適當的答覆。

字彙 responsible 負責任的

8

Is it possible to review my report sometime this week?

(A) Of course. What time will be good for you?

(B) Sorry. I already finished it.

(C) I was busy.

這週可以找時間看一下我的報告嗎？

(A) 當然好，你何時方便？

(B) 抱歉，我已經完成了。

(C) 我當時在忙。

解析

本題詢問是否能在這週看一下報告。(A) 反問對方什麼時候比較好，故為適當的答覆。(C) 使用過去式、(B) 表示已經完成，皆不適合作為答案。

9

Will you be free for next week's dinner?

(A) No, I was busy.

(B) I need more time.

(C) I will be away for 2 weeks.

下週的晚餐，你能來嗎？

(A) 不，我當時在忙。

(B) 我需要更多時間。

(C) 我會有兩週不在。

解析

本題詢問下週晚餐時間是否有空來吃飯。(C) 回答自己有兩週的時間不在，間接表示自己無法出席，故為適當的答覆。(A) 乍聽之下像是適當的答覆，但因為時態不符，故無法作為答案。

10

Were there a lot of questions after the presentation?

(A) I am not good at it.

(B) There were many participants.

(C) Yes, that's why it finished late.

簡報結束後，有很多人提問嗎？

(A) 我不擅長。

(B) 有很多人參加。

(C) 是的，所以才很晚結束。

解析

本題詢問簡報結束後是否有很多人提問。(C) 回答 Yes 後，表示這正是較晚結束的原因，故為正確答案。

字彙 participant 參加者

05 助動詞開頭問句   p.52

Do / Have

STEP 1 題型演練

(1 (B)   2 (A)   3 (A)   4 (A)   5 (B))

1

你有參加去年的金融研討會嗎？

(A) 在義大利的羅馬。

(B) 有，我去年十月去的。

2

你在你的電腦上安裝好新軟體了嗎？

(A) 是的，我昨天有時間。

(B) 他是位很好的技術人員。

3

你有空和我一起審閱這份報告嗎？

(A) 要 3 點以後。

(B) 在我桌上。

4

那家餐廳週日有開門營業嗎？

(A) 我要問一下。

(B) 午餐準備好了。

5

你接受了自由作家的文章嗎？

(A) 有幾名應徵者。

(B) 不，我還沒看。

1 (A) (C)	**2** (C)	**3** (B)
4 (A) (B)	**5** (B) (C)	**6** (A) (B)

1

Did you <u>meet</u> with your <u>accountant</u>?
(A) No, but I will.
(B) <u>Sales</u> are low.
(C) Yes, this morning.

你和你的會計師碰過面了嗎？
(A) 還沒，但我會的。
(B) 業績很差。
(C) 是的，今天早上見了。

解析

本題為 did 開頭的一般動詞問句，詢問是否跟會計師碰過面。(A) 表示還沒碰面、(C) 表示今天早上見過，皆為適當的答覆。

2

<u>Did you work</u> for KH Technology before?
(A) <u>The interview is</u> at 2 P.M.
(B) No, I like my job.
(C) Yes, for three years.

你以前在 KH 科技上班嗎？
(A) 面試是下午 2 點。
(B) 不，我喜歡我的工作。
(C) 是的，做了三年。

解析

面對 do / does / did 開頭的問句，可以用 Yes 或 No 來回答。本題詢問是否有在特定的公司工作過，(C) 回答 Yes，並提及曾工作多久，故為適當的答覆。

3

Do they <u>lock the storage room</u> at 6 o'clock?
(A) There is a lot of room.
(B) Ask Tim in the Maintenance Department.
(C) Mostly <u>boxes of paper</u>.

他們會在 6 點把儲藏室鎖起來嗎？
(A) 空間很大。
(B) 問維修部的提姆。
(C) 大部份都是紙箱。

解析

本題詢問是否會在 6 點時把門鎖上。(B) 要求詢問他人，故為正確答案。像這類採用間接回答方式的選項，經常都是正確答案。

字彙 storage room 儲藏室
Maintenance Department 維修部

4

<u>Has</u> the new cell phone model <u>been released</u>?
(A) Sorry. We don't have it yet.
(B) Yes, it's down the hall on your right.
(C) I bought a new laptop.

新款手機已經上市了嗎？
(A) 抱歉，我們還沒有開賣。
(B) 是的，在大廳那頭，您的右手邊。
(C) 我買了一台新的筆電。

解析

本題詢問新款手機是否已經上市。(A) 表示目前店內還沒有、(B) 告知對方新上市的手機放在什麼位置，皆為正確答案。

字彙 release 上市

5

Do you want to <u>apply for</u> our store's membership card?
(A) We can <u>deliver it by Monday</u>.
(B) No, thanks.
(C) Yes, that would be great.

您想申辦我們店裡的會員卡嗎？
(A) 我們最晚週一可以送。
(B) 不用，謝謝。
(C) 是的，如果可以就太棒了。

解析

本題詢問是否要申辦會員卡。(B) 表示拒絕、(C) 給予肯定答覆，皆為正確答案。(A) 故意使用 deliver（運送、投遞），與題目中的 store（商店）有所關聯，意圖使人產生混淆。

字彙 apply for 應徵、申請
deliver 運送、投遞

6

Has Mr. Shin <u>arrived in</u> New York yet?
(A) Yes, a few hours ago.
(B) No, he is arriving tomorrow.
(C) He'd be <u>happy to</u>.

申先生抵達紐約了沒？
(A) 是的，幾個小時前到了。
(B) 沒有，他明天才到。
(C) 他會很樂意。

解析

本題詢問 Mr. Shin（申先生）是否已經抵達。(A) 表示他已經抵達、(B) 表示他明天才會抵達，皆為正確答案。

Can / Could / May / Should

STEP 1 題型演練

| 1 (B) | 2 (A) | 3 (B) | 4 (A) | 5 (B) |

1

你下週可以載我去上班嗎？
(A) 好，你可以騎我的機車。
(B) 我的車昨天故障了。

2

我們應該搬到比較安靜的地方嗎？
(A) 那是個好主意。
(B) 他們搬到新的公寓去了。

3

我可以幫你什麼嗎？
(A) 打電話給店員。
(B) 目前不用。

4

你可以教我怎麼啟動投影機嗎？
(A) 我五分鐘後可以。
(B) 是的，在 608 號室。

5

我可以從我的飯店房間打國際電話嗎？
(A) 您可以在這裡付款。
(B) 可以，是免費的。

STEP 3 聽寫練習

| 1 (C) | 2 (B) (C) | 3 (B) |
| 4 (A) | 5 (A) (C) | 6 (A) (B) |

1

Can you take me to our client's office this afternoon?
(A) Our customers are very pleased.
(B) It is near the post office.
(C) I didn't bring my car.

你今天下午可以載我去我們客戶的辦公室嗎？
(A) 我們的顧客非常滿意。
(B) 那裡離郵局很近。
(C) 我沒有開車來。

解析

本題用問句請求對方載自己一程。(C) 表示沒有開車來，委婉拒絕請求，故為正確答案。(A) 故意使用 customers（顧客），為 client（客戶）的同義字，意圖使人產生混淆；(B) 重複使用 office，屬於陷阱選項。

字彙 customer 顧客　pleased 高興的、滿意的

2

May I take a look at the lab test results?
(A) Where is the laboratory?
(B) Go ahead.
(C) They are on your desk.

我可以看一下實驗室檢測結果嗎？
(A) 實驗室在哪裡？
(B) 請看。
(C) 在你桌上。

解析

may 開頭的問句用來請求對方的同意。(B) 回答「Go ahead」屬於肯定答覆，表示同意對方觀看檢測結果；(C) 告知檢測結果放在什麼地方，兩者皆為正確答案。

字彙 laboratory 實驗室

3

Can you update the new sales figures this morning?
(A) We did promotional events.
(B) Please wait until this afternoon.
(C) That's such a bargain.

你今天早上可以更新一下銷售數據嗎？
(A) 我們舉行了促銷活動。
(B) 請等到今天下午。
(C) 真是太划算了。

解析

can 開頭的問句用來詢問可能與否。本題詢問能否更新銷售數據，(B) 要求等到下午，符合題意。

字彙 promotional 促銷的、廣告宣傳的
　　　　bargain 買賣、交易

4

Should I write a proposal to develop our new product's design?
(A) I think that's a great idea.
(B) I'm planning to buy it.
(C) The color is not too bright.

我應該寫個提案來擬定我們新產品的設計嗎？
(A) 我覺得那是個好主意。
(B) 我打算買下來。
(C) 顏色不會太亮。

解析

should 開頭的問句用來表示建議。本題詢問是否應該撰寫提案，(A) 給予肯定答覆，故為正確答案。

5

Could you review the advertisement plans we created?
(A) I will do it first thing tomorrow morning.
(B) For twenty minutes.
(C) I did it this morning.

你可以審閱一下我們製作的廣告方案嗎？
(A) 我明天一早就看。
(B) 要 20 分鐘。
(C) 我今天早上看過了。

解析

本題詢問對方是否能看一下廣告方案。(A) 表示「明天一早就看」、(C) 表示已經看過，皆為正確答案。

6

Can you attend the awards ceremony on Wednesday?
(A) Sure. What time is it?
(B) Well, I don't think I can make it.
(C) Congratulations.

你可以參加週三的頒獎典禮嗎？
(A) 沒問題，幾點開始？
(B) 嗯，我覺得我沒有辦法去。
(C) 恭喜。

解析

本題詢問是否參加頒獎典禮。(A) 給予肯定答覆並詢問時間、(B) 表示拒絕，皆為適當的答覆。「make it」可以用來表示「參加」之意。

字彙 awards ceremony 頒獎典禮

實戰演練   p.56

1 (B)	2 (A)	3 (A)	4 (C)	5 (C)
6 (A)	7 (A)	8 (C)	9 (A)	10 (A)

1

Could you show me how to operate this machine?
(A) It is on the second floor.
(B) I'm new to this, too.
(C) Suzanne called you earlier.

你可以教我怎麼操作這台機器嗎？
(A) 在二樓。
(B) 我也不熟悉這台機器。
(C) 蘇珊稍早打過電話給你。

解析

本題詢問操作機器的方法。(B) 表示自己沒怎麼用過、不太清楚，為最適當的答覆。(A) 告知機器放置的位置，與 (C) 的回答均與題目內容無關。

字彙 operate 操作

2

Should we sit outside on the patio to have lunch?
(A) Isn't it going to be cold?
(B) I'll have coffee.
(C) Three people are invited.

我們應該坐在外面的露台吃午餐嗎？
(A) 不是要變冷了嗎？
(B) 我要咖啡。
(C) 有三個人受邀。

解析

本題使用問句表示建議。(A) 反問對方天氣「不是要變冷了嗎？」，帶有否定對方建議的意味，故為正確答案。採用反問的方式來回答，經常都是正確答案。

字彙 patio 露台

3

Did you see your dentist this afternoon?
(A) Oh, no. I forgot.
(B) Please remind me later.
(C) I have a fever.

你今天下午去看牙醫了嗎？
(A) 噢，不，我忘了。
(B) 請稍後提醒我。
(C) 我發燒了。

解析

本題為一般問句，詢問對方是否去看了牙醫。(A) 回答忘記了，表示自己沒去看，故為正確答案。

字彙 dentist 牙醫   remind 提醒

4

May I leave the office a little earlier today?
(A) In fact, she was a few minutes late.
(B) It shouldn't take long.
(C) Sure. Are you okay?

我今天可以提早一點下班嗎？
(A) 其實她遲到了幾分鐘。
(B) 應該不會太久。
(C) 沒問題，你還好嗎？

解析

may 開頭的問句用來尋求對方的同意。本題詢問是否可以提早下班，(C) 表示同意對方提早下班，並反問對方的身體狀況，故為適當的答覆。

字彙 **take long** 花很久時間

5

Do you recommend going to the new French restaurant?
(A) You need three recommendation letters.
(B) Why don't we meet at 3:30?
(C) Yes, it's the best place I've ever been.

你推薦去那間新開幕的法國餐廳嗎？
(A) 你需要有三封推薦信。
(B) 我們何不 3 點半碰面？
(C) 是的，那是我去過最棒的餐廳。

解析

本題詢問是否推薦新開幕的法國餐廳。(C) 給予肯定答覆，表示是最棒的餐廳，故為正確答案。(A) 故意使用 recommendation（推薦），為題目動詞 recommend 衍生的名詞，意圖使人產生混淆；(B) 提到見面時間，答非所問。

字彙 **recommend** 推薦、建議
recommendation letter 推薦信

6

Have you ordered advance tickets for the opening game of the championship?
(A) Yes, a month ago.
(B) The show is on Sunday.
(C) Your order is ready.

你訂好錦標賽開幕戰的預售票了嗎？
(A) 是的，一個月前就訂了。
(B) 表演是在週日。
(C) 你訂的貨已經準備好了。

解析

本題詢問是否有事先訂好票。(A) 表示一個月前就訂了，故為適當的答覆。(B) 故意使用 show（表演），與 game（比賽）有所關聯；(C) 重複使用 order，意圖使人產生混淆。

字彙 **order** 訂購　**advance ticket** 預售票
opening game 開幕賽

7

Do you think the manual is too complicated?
(A) It should be simplified.
(B) No, it was created by Mark.
(C) Just follow the instructions.

你覺得使用手冊會太複雜嗎？
(A) 應該要簡化一點。
(B) 不是，是馬克製作的。
(C) 遵照操作指南就行了。

解析

本題詢問使用手冊內容是否太複雜。(A) 表示同意，認為應該簡化，故為正確答案。(B) 的內容答非所問；(C) 故意使用 instruction（操作指南），與 manual（使用手冊）的意思相近，意圖使人產生混淆。

字彙 **manual** 使用手冊　**complicated** 複雜的
simplify 簡化　**instruction** 操作指南

8

Have you sent out the invitations to Ms. Gray's farewell party?
(A) She is retired.
(B) At the Hill Hotel.
(C) I don't have the guest list.

你把萬瑞女士歡送會的邀請函寄出去了嗎？
(A) 她退休了。
(B) 在希爾飯店。
(C) 我沒有賓客名單。

解析

本題使用現在完成式，詢問是否已將邀請函寄出。(C) 回答沒有賓客名單，表示還沒寄出，故為正確答案。(A) 故意使用 retired（退休），僅與「farewell party」（歡送會）有所關聯，屬於陷阱選項；(B) 適合用來回答 where 開頭詢問地點的問句。

字彙 **invitation** 邀請函　**farewell party** 歡送會
retire 退休

9

Can you make the speech no longer than twenty minutes?

(A) **Okay, I will keep it short.**
(B) It was at least thirty minutes.
(C) The speech was impressive.

你可以讓演講不超過 20 分鐘嗎？
(A) **好的，我會長話短說。**
(B) 至少 30 分鐘。
(C) 演講令人印象深刻。

解析

本題用問句請求對方縮短演講時間。(A) 表示願意縮短時間，故為正確答案。(B) 雖然可以用來表示演講時間，但是使用的是過去式，不適合當作答案；(C) 僅重複使用 speech（演講），意圖使人產生混淆。

字彙 speech 演講　at least 至少
impressive 令人印象深刻的

10

Does this parade happen every year?

(A) **Every two years.**
(B) I like crowds.
(C) It started yesterday.

這個遊行每年都有嗎？
(A) **每兩年舉辦一次。**
(B) 我喜歡群眾。
(C) 昨天開始的。

解析

本題詢問是否每年都有舉辦遊行。(A) 表示兩年舉辦一次，為適當的答覆。

字彙 parade 遊行　crowd 人群、大眾

多益實戰單字 PART 2 UNIT ❶ - ❺　p.58

A
1 (B)　　**2** (A)　　**3** (A)　　**4** (A)　　**5** (B)

B
1 operate
2 building directory
3 farewell party
4 sign up for
5 ask for

C
1 has not been decided
2 What do you think of
3 in charge of organizing
4 are we supposed to meet
5 Which of these products

06 間接問句／選擇性疑問句　p.59

間接問句

STEP 1 題型演練

| 1 (A) | 2 (B) | 3 (A) | 4 (A) | 5 (B) |

1

你知道下一班火車何時來嗎？
(A) **大約 30 分鐘後。**
(B) 還沒確定。

2

你有聽說是誰要發表演說嗎？
(A) 他是一位優秀的講者。
(B) **是達賓斯先生。**

3

你可以告訴我會議要在哪裡舉行嗎？
(A) **在會議廳。**
(B) 抱歉，我當時沒辦法。

4

我能否請問你在哪裡上班？
(A) **我目前在待業中。**
(B) 我正在做這個專案。

5

你可以告訴我銀行幾點會開門嗎？
(A) 現在打烊了。
(B) **通常是早上 9 點。**

STEP 3 聽寫練習

1 (B)	2 (A)	3 (C)
4 (B) (C)	5 (C)	6 (B) (C)

1

Do you know why the company is hiring a new manager?

(A) We are still waiting.
(B) It needs one to lead a new team.
(C) Because it isn't ready.

33

你知道公司為什麼新聘了一位經理嗎？
(A) 我們還在等。
(B) 公司需要一位經理來帶領新的團隊。
(C) 因為還沒準備好。

解析

本題詢問對方是否知道公司新聘了一位經理的原因。(B) 表示需要帶領新團隊的人，告知具體的原因，故為正確答案。該選項使用代名詞 it 來代替「the company」（公司）。

字彙 **manager** 經理

2

Can you tell me how often the bus runs?
(A) Every 20 minutes.
(B) The traffic is awful.
(C) Public transportation would be nice.

你可以告訴我公車多久來一班嗎？
(A) 每 20 分鐘一班。
(B) 交通狀況很糟。
(C) 大眾運輸很好。

解析

本題要求對方告知公車發車的間隔時間。(A) 回答「每 20 分鐘一班」，故為正確答案。

3

Do you know what the sales figures are like this quarter?
(A) The Sales Department.
(B) I didn't like it.
(C) I haven't heard anything about them.

你知道這一季的銷售數字怎麼樣嗎？
(A) 業務部。
(B) 我不喜歡。
(C) 我還沒聽到任何消息。

解析

本題詢問這一季的銷售數字。(C) 表示自己還沒聽到任何消息，故為正確答案。該選項使用代名詞 them 來代替「sales figures」（銷售數字）。

4

Did you hear who is coming to the R&D Department?
(A) I didn't hear from her.
(B) I haven't heard yet.
(C) Mr. Cummings will.

你有聽說誰要來研發部嗎？
(A) 我沒有她的消息。
(B) 我還沒聽說。
(C) 是康明斯先生。

解析

本題詢問是否有聽說誰要來研發部。(B) 表示還沒聽說、(C) 告知要來的對象，皆為正確答案。(A)「hear from」的意思為「收到（某人）的消息或信等」。

5

Could you tell me why you didn't like the proposal?
(A) I wasn't told about it.
(B) He proposed it.
(C) The budget is an issue.

你可以告訴我你為什麼不喜歡這個提案嗎？
(A) 沒人告訴我。
(B) 他提議的。
(C) 預算是一個問題。

解析

本題為「could you」開頭的問句，請求對方告知對提案不滿的原因。(C) 提出具體原因，故為正確答案。

字彙 **issue** 問題、爭議

6

Do you happen to know where the contracts are?
(A) You've already answered it.
(B) They are in the top drawer.
(C) Actually, I was looking for them, too.

你知道合約在哪裡嗎？
(A) 你已經回應過了。
(B) 在最上面的抽屜裡。
(C) 其實我當時也在找。

解析

「Do you happen to know . . . ?」為向別人打聽事情時委婉的問法。本題詢問合約放在哪裡，(B) 告知放在最上面的抽屜裡、(C) 表示自己也在找合約，皆為正確答案。

選擇性疑問句

STEP 1 題型演練

1 (A)	2 (B)	3 (B)	4 (A)	5 (A)

1

你要看報紙還是雜誌？
(A) 都不要，我想要放鬆。
(B) 我兩個都試過了。

2

你比較喜歡早上工作，還是下午？
(A) 我好累。
(B) 我習慣早起。

3

您要付現還是刷卡？
(A) 這個沒有付錢。
(B) 我的現金不夠。

4

你要牛肉還是雞肉？
(A) 都不要，我不餓。
(B) 我兩種都吃過了。

5

你想要我幫你，還是你可以自己一個人做？
(A) 我可以自己來。
(B) 我會和你一起。

STEP 3 聽寫練習

1 (A) (C)	2 (A)	3 (B)
4 (C)	5 (C)	6 (A) (B)

1

Would you like to have the red bag or the blue one?
(A) I like neither.
(B) I don't have time for it.
(C) I will go with the red one.

你想要紅色的包包，還是藍色的？
(A) 兩個我都不要。
(B) 我沒時間做。
(C) 我選紅色的。

解析

本題問句要求從紅色包包和藍色包包中擇一。(A) 表示兩個都不喜歡、(C) 表示選擇紅色包包，皆為正確答案。題目為選擇性疑問句時，可以回答「兩者皆非」作為答案。

字彙 go with 選擇、接受

2

Are you going on a business trip on Tuesday or Thursday?
(A) Neither. It has been canceled.
(B) I don't enjoy taking trips.
(C) Let's do that first.

你是週二還是週四去出差？
(A) 都不是，出差取消了。
(B) 我不喜歡旅行。
(C) 我們先做那個。

解析

本題詢問出差時間為週二還是週四。(A) 表示兩者皆非，故為正確答案。(B) 重複使用 trip（旅行），但並非答案；(C) 的回答與題目內容無關。

3

Would you prefer to work in Finance or Accounting?
(A) No, thanks.
(B) Anywhere is fine.
(C) I don't want to go there.

你比較想在財務部工作，還是會計部？
(A) 不用，謝謝。
(B) 哪裡都可以。
(C) 我不想去那裡。

解析

本題詢問對方想在兩個部門中的哪個部門工作。(B) 表示兩個都可以，故為正確答案。選擇性疑問句的回答中，若使用 either 或 any，指的是無論選哪一個都可以。

4

Who do you think is more qualified for the job, Georgia or you?
(A) The more, the better.
(B) Both of us are unhappy.
(C) It's hard to say.

你覺得誰更能勝任這份工作，喬琪亞還是你？
(A) 愈多愈好。
(B) 我們兩個都不快樂。
(C) 很難說。

解析

本題詢問 Georgia（喬琪亞）或對方之中，誰更勝任這份工作。(C) 表示難以回答這個問題，故為正確答案。面對難以回答的問題時，可以使用「It's hard to say.」答覆。

5

Would you <u>rather take</u> a taxi or <u>walk in the rain</u>?

(A) I'd <u>rather not say</u>.

(B) My <u>schedule</u> is <u>flexible</u>.

(C) I don't have a preference.

你比較想要搭計程車，還是要冒著雨走？

(A) 我寧願不要說。

(B) 我的時間很有彈性。

(C) 我沒有特別偏好。

解析

(C) 表示面對兩項選擇並沒有特別偏好哪一方，故為正確答案。「I don't have a preference」的意思為「我沒有特別偏好」，表示無論選哪一個都可以。

6

Will you be able to <u>help me now</u>, or <u>should I wait</u> more?

(A) I will be ready in a few minutes.

(B) I can do it right away.

(C) I am not <u>patient enough</u>.

你現在可以幫我，還是我要再等等？

(A) 我再幾分鐘就好了。

(B) 我現在就能幫忙。

(C) 我不夠有耐心。

解析

本題詢問對方能現在就幫忙，還是要再等一下。(A) 表示再幾分鐘後就好、(B) 表示現在就能幫忙，皆為適當的答覆。

字彙 patient 有耐心的

實戰演練 p.63

1 (A)	2 (C)	3 (A)	4 (B)	5 (A)
6 (C)	7 (B)	8 (A)	9 (C)	10 (A)

1

Do <u>you want me to</u> mail this, or <u>will you go</u> to the post office yourself?

(A) Jack will mail it this afternoon.

(B) I <u>am fond of</u> it.

(C) The <u>delivery</u> will <u>cost a lot</u>.

你要我去寄這個，還是你要自己去郵局？

(A) 傑克今天下午會去寄。

(B) 我很喜歡它。

(C) 郵寄要花很多錢。

解析

本題詢問對方希望自己幫忙寄，還是對方要親自去郵局寄。(A) 提到第三人 Jack（傑克），表示他今天下午會寄，故為適當的答覆。(B) 的內容答非所問；(C) 故意使用 delivery（郵寄），與題目內容有關，屬於陷阱選項。

字彙 be fond of 喜歡……   delivery 郵寄

2

Can you <u>tell me why</u> you <u>decided to leave</u> the firm?

(A) I <u>stopped working</u>.

(B) There is <u>no need to rush</u>.

(C) I had trouble with my supervisor.

你可以告訴我，你為什麼決定離開公司嗎？

(A) 我不再工作了。

(B) 不需要趕時間。

(C) 我和我主管合不來。

解析

本題詢問決定離開公司的原因。(C) 表示自己跟主管合不來，故為正確答案。

字彙 firm 公司   supervisor 主管

3

Would <u>you like to have</u> dinner <u>tomorrow</u> or sometime <u>next week</u>?

(A) I am free tomorrow.

(B) I <u>don't think so</u>.

(C) Dinner <u>would be nice</u>.

你想要明天吃晚餐，還是下週再另外找個時間？

(A) 我明天有空。

(B) 我想不是。

(C) 吃晚餐就好了。

解析

本題詢問明天或下週，哪個時間有空一起吃晚餐。(A) 表示明天有空，為適當的答覆。(B) 的內容答非所問；(C) 只是重複使用 dinner（晚餐），屬於陷阱選項。

4

Did you <u>hear who</u> is going to <u>apply for</u> the position?

(A) No one <u>showed up</u>.

(B) Jack in HR.

(C) The <u>application forms</u> are over there.

你有聽說是誰要應徵這個職位嗎？

(A) 沒有人出席。

(B) 人力資源部的傑克。

(C) 申請表在那邊。

解析

本題詢問誰要應徵那個職位。(B) 提到應徵者的名字，故為正確答案。請特別留意，千萬不要一聽到「no one」（沒有人），就選擇 (A) 作為答案。

字彙 apply for 應徵　position 職位
application form 申請表

5

Should I order the office supplies today or next week?
(A) We can wait till next week.
(B) The stationery store is closed.
(C) You shouldn't do that.

我應該今天訂購辦公室用品，還是下週再訂？
(A) 我們可以等到下週。
(B) 文具店打烊了。
(C) 你不應該這麼做。

解析

本題詢問要今天、還是下週訂購辦公室用品。(A) 表示等到下週再説，故為正確答案。(B)「stationery store」意為「文具店」，與「office supplies」（辦公室用品）有所關聯，但並非正確答案。

6

Do you know when the next train is scheduled to leave?
(A) They will come soon.
(B) We are running late.
(C) Let me check on that for you.

你知道下一班火車預定何時發車嗎？
(A) 它們很快就到了。
(B) 我們快遲到了。
(C) 讓我幫你查一下。

解析

本題詢問下一班火車何時發車。(C) 表示要查看看，故為正確答案。(A) 主詞使用複數形 they（它們），與題目的單數主詞「the next train」（下一班火車）不符，因此不適合作為答案。

7

May I ask what kind of job you had previously?
(A) I have done it before.
(B) I was in marketing.
(C) Please answer me.

我可以問一下你之前做過什麼樣的工作嗎？
(A) 我以前做過。
(B) 我做過行銷。
(C) 請回答我。

解析

本題詢問先前從事過什麼工作。(B) 表示做過行銷方面的工作，故為正確答案。(A) 並未明確告知從事過什麼樣的工作，因此不能作為答案；(C) 故意使用 answer（回答），與題目中的 ask（詢問）有所關聯，但並非答案。

8

Can I leave now, or do you want me to stay a little longer?
(A) It's up to you.
(B) I can't live here.
(C) That's all I know.

我是現在可以離開，還是你要我再多留一會？
(A) 你自己決定。
(B) 我沒辦法住在這裡。
(C) 我知道的就這麼多。

解析

本題詢問現在可以離開，還是得再多留一會。(A) 表示看對方方便、讓對方自己決定，為適當的答覆。(B) 故意使用 live（住），與 leave（離開）的發音相近，屬於陷阱選項。

字彙 it's up to you 由你決定、看你自己

9

Do you know where the nearest convenience store is?
(A) Just a few things.
(B) Actually, it is not on sale.
(C) I am not familiar with this area.

你知道最近的便利商店在哪裡嗎？
(A) 只有一些東西。
(B) 事實上，並沒有在特價。
(C) 我對這一區不熟。

解析

本題詢問鄰近的便利商店位置。(C) 表示對這個區域不熟，故為正確答案。當題目詢問地點時，答案經常會是：「I'm not familiar with this area.」。

字彙 convenience store 便利商店

10

Do you <u>need some help with</u> the report, or <u>can you
do</u> it yourself?

(A) <u>I can handle it.</u>

(B) <u>Let's find out.</u>

(C) <u>I did it myself.</u>

你報告需要幫忙，還是你可以自己做？

(A) 我可以處理。

(B) 讓我們查清楚。

(C) 我自己完成的。

解析

本題詢問對方的報告是否需要幫忙，還是能夠獨力完
成。(A) 表示自己能夠處理，故為正確答案。(C) 使用
過去式，因此不適合作為答案。

字彙 handle 處理　find out 查明（真相等）

07 附加問句／否定疑問句　　p.65

附加問句

STEP 1 題型演練

1 (B)　2 (A)　3 (A)　4 (B)　5 (A)

1

你還沒交作業，對嗎？

(A) 面試很順利。

(B) 對，也許要到吃完午餐後。

2

你今晚沒有要加班，對嗎？

(A) 對啊，我有點累。

(B) 不對，我準備要下班了。

3

梅先生加薪了，不是嗎？

(A) 你從哪裡聽來的？

(B) 是的，他調到業務團隊了。

4

珍還沒有盤點存貨，對嗎？

(A) 你可以拿兩個。

(B) 對，她看起來很忙。

5

我應該取消會議，不是嗎？

(A) 那樣比較好。

(B) 不是在 3 號室嗎？

STEP 3 聽寫練習

| 1 (A) (B) | 2 (C) | 3 (A) (C) |
| 4 (A) (C) | 5 (A) (B) (C) | 6 (A) (B) |

1

<u>You've been to</u> Spain, haven't you?

(A) <u>Yes, three times.</u>

(B) <u>I'm afraid</u> I haven't.

(C) He just <u>left the office.</u>

你去過西班牙，不是嗎？

(A) 是的，去過三次。

(B) 很遺憾，我沒去過。

(C) 他剛離開辦公室。

解析

題目為附加問句時，請務必專心聆聽問題的內容。也
就是說，不用在意「haven't you」的部分，僅針對
是否去過西班牙來回答。有去過就回答 Yes、沒去過
則回答 No，因此答案選 (A) Yes, three times. 和 (B)
I'm afraid I haven't.。答案經常出現像 (B) 這類省略
Yes 或 No 來回答的選項。

2

There is a post office around the corner, <u>isn't there</u>?

(A) <u>By express mail.</u>

(B) The shop is closed.

(C) <u>There used to be one</u> down the road.

附近有一間郵局，不是嗎？

(A) 寄快捷郵件。

(B) 商店打烊了。

(C) 路的那頭以前有一間。

解析

本題欲確認郵局的位置。(C) 為說話者回憶路的那頭
之前有一間（不確定現在還有沒有），建議對方去看
看，故為正確答案。「There used to be」是把「used
to」併入「There is」的句型。因「used to」後面要
加原形動詞，須把 is 改為 be，表示「曾經有……」。

字彙 around the corner 在附近

3

You <u>didn't call</u> Dr. Petal, <u>did you</u>?

(A) <u>Yes, this morning.</u>

(B) I need to see the dentist.

(C) <u>Am I supposed to?</u>

你沒有打電話給派托醫生，對嗎？

(A) 有啊，今天早上。

(B) 我需要看牙醫。

(C) 我應該要打嗎？

解析

如果有打過電話，便要回答 Yes。(A) 表示上午打過電話，故為正確答案。另外，「be supposed to」的意思為「應該……」。(C) 以此反問對方是否應該打電話，也是正確的答案。

4

You haven't booked your flight, have you?
(A) Actually, I just did.
(B) I borrowed a couple of books.
(C) No, I've been busy lately.

你還沒有訂機票，對嗎？
(A) 事實上，我剛剛訂了。
(B) 我借了幾本書。
(C) 對，我最近很忙。

解析

本題詢問是否訂了機票。(A) 表示剛剛訂了、(C) 表示最近太忙還沒訂，皆為正確答案。題目中的 book 是動詞，意思為「預訂」，(B) 當中的 book 則是名詞，意思為「書」。

5

The projector can be fixed, can't it?
(A) We might need a new one.
(B) I need to look into it.
(C) I just called a technician.

投影機可以修，不是嗎？
(A) 我們也許需要買台新的。
(B) 我需要詳細檢查一下。
(C) 我剛打電話找了技術人員。

解析

(A) 表示無法修理，得買一台新的投影機、(B) 表示需要檢查看看、(C) 表示剛請技術人員來修理了，皆為正確答案。

6

Mr. Anderson hasn't given you the files, has he?
(A) Yes, I got them yesterday.
(B) I think he forgot.
(C) The documents should be kept safely.

安德森先生還沒有給你檔案，對嗎？
(A) 不，我昨天拿到了。
(B) 我想他忘記了。
(C) 文件應該要好好保管。

解析

只要暫時忽略「has he」，並把問句改成肯定直述句，便不會搞混要用 Yes 還是 No 來回答。題目問的是「是否有給檔案」，(A) 直接表示昨天就收到了、(B) 回答 Mr. Anderson（安德森先生）似乎忘記了，表示還沒有給，兩者皆為正確答案。

否定疑問句

STEP 1 題型演練

1 (B)	2 (A)	3 (B)	4 (A)	5 (A)

1

旁邊不是有家百貨公司嗎？
(A) 道路現在封閉了。
(B) 有，就在附近。

2

你還沒把包裹寄去給福特先生嗎？
(A) 抱歉，我馬上去寄。
(B) 是的，在樓下。

3

你的車上週不是故障了嗎？
(A) 我已經做了。
(B) 是的，車現在還在修車廠。

4

你不是和醫生約今天早上嗎？
(A) 謝謝你提醒我。
(B) 他是一位很優秀的外科醫生。

5

戴安不是通常都 3 點到嗎？
(A) 是的，但她今天生病了。
(B) 我們上班要遲到了。

STEP 3 聽寫練習

1 (B) (C)	2 (A) (C)	3 (A) (B)
4 (B) (C)	5 (A) (B)	6 (A)

1

Why wasn't Ms. Rice at work this morning?
(A) At three in the afternoon.
(B) She called in sick.
(C) I think Kelly might know.

萊斯女士今天早上為什麼沒上班？
(A) 下午 3 點。
(B) 她打電話請了病假。
(C) 我想凱莉也許知道。

PART

2

07 附加問句／否定疑問句

解析

本題詢問沒來上班的原因。(B) 表示她請病假、(C) 提到另一個人的名字，表示她可能知道原因，皆為適當的答覆。

2

Aren't you supposed to be on vacation?
(A) Yes, but I rescheduled it.
(B) I'm going to Hawaii.
(C) No, it is next week.

你不是應該在度假嗎？
(A) 對，但我重新安排了時間。
(B) 我要去夏威夷。
(C) 不，是下週。

解析

「be supposed to」意思為「（被認為）應該……」。本題以否定句詢問，如果現在應該休假須回答 Yes，沒有則回答 No。(A) 回答 Yes，接著解釋已經調整日程、(C) 回答 No，接著表示下週才要休假，皆為正確答案。

字彙 reschedule 重新安排……的時間

3

Can't you meet with the clients after lunch?
(A) Sorry. I am busy all afternoon.
(B) I don't think so.
(C) Not that I know of.

你午餐後不能去見客戶嗎？
(A) 抱歉，我整個下午都要忙。
(B) 我覺得沒辦法。
(C) 就我所知不是那樣。

解析

(A) 和 (B) 皆使用否定答覆，表示無法與客戶見面，故為正確答案。

4

Shouldn't we organize Ms. Hunt's retirement party?
(A) She is on her way.
(B) I am working on it.
(C) She said she didn't want any.

我們不是應該要籌備杭特女士的退休歡送會嗎？
(A) 她在路上了。
(B) 我正在安排。
(C) 她說她不想要歡送會。

解析

(B) 表示自己正在安排、(C) 轉達本人表示不需要為她準備，皆為適當的答覆。

字彙 organize 籌備　**retirement** 退休

5

Aren't the volunteers coming today?
(A) No, they changed their minds.
(B) Not until next Monday.
(C) Why don't you sign up?

義工今天不是要來嗎？
(A) 沒有，他們改變心意了。
(B) 要到下週一才會來。
(C) 你為何不報名？

解析

(A) 回答 No，表示義工今天不會來，接著解釋是因為他們改變心意才決定不來，故為正確答案。另外，(B) 表示到下週一才會來，也是適當的答覆。

字彙 volunteer 志願者、義工

6

Aren't you going to attend the conference in London?
(A) No, it has been canceled.
(B) She isn't going.
(C) Mr. Lim organized it.

你不是要去參加倫敦的研討會嗎？
(A) 不去，研討會取消了。
(B) 她不去。
(C) 是林先生籌辦的。

解析

(A) 使用否定答覆，表示不會參加會議，故為正確答案。(B) 的主詞為 she，因此不能作為答案。

字彙 attend 出席、參加

實戰演練   p.69

1 (C)	2 (C)	3 (A)	4 (B)	5 (B)
6 (A)	7 (A)	8 (A)	9 (B)	10 (A)

1

Doesn't Helen usually leave the office at five?
(A) She is my supervisor.
(B) No, we start at four.
(C) Yes, but she has a deadline to meet today.

海倫不是通常都 5 點下班嗎？
(A) 她是我的主管。
(B) 不是，我們 4 點開始。
(C) 是的，但是今天她有個工作要趕在截止期限前完成。

解析

本題詢問 Helen（海倫）是否通常在 5 點下班。(C) 回答 Yes，表示同意該事實，接著表示為配合截止期限，今天才比較晚下班，故為正確答案。

字彙 supervisor 主管　　deadline 截止期限

2

These umbrellas <u>are produced</u> by our new supplier, <u>aren't they?</u>
(A) No, it <u>is not raining</u>.
(B) Maybe next month.
(C) No, the old one made them.

這些雨傘是我們的新供應商製造的，不是嗎？
(A) 沒有，現在沒下雨。
(B) 也許下個月。
(C) 不是，是原來的供應商製造的。

解析

(C) 表示由先前的供應商製作，並非新的供應商，為適當的答覆。千萬不要因為聽到題目中出現 umbrella（雨傘），就誤選 (A) 作為答案。(B) 的內容答非所問。

字彙 supplier 供應商

3

Ms. Forster <u>hasn't approved the budget proposal</u>, has she?
(A) She did yesterday.
(B) About <u>six copies</u>.
(C) At the staff meeting.

佛斯特女士還沒有批准預算案，對嗎？
(A) 她昨天批准了。
(B) 大約六份。
(C) 在員工會議上。

解析

本題詢問預算案是否已經被批准。(A) 省略 Yes/No，直接表示昨天已批准，故為正確答案。

字彙 approve 同意、批准
　　　 budget proposal 預算案

4

You said the <u>proposal would be ready</u> this week, <u>didn't you?</u>
(A) No, he will <u>reschedule the event</u>.
(B) Yes, it is <u>on your desk.</u>
(C) Five days ago.

你說計畫書這週會準備好，不是嗎？
(A) 不，他會重新安排活動的時間。
(B) 是的，在你桌上。
(C) 五天前。

解析

本題詢問對方是否說過這週會準備好計畫書。(B) 回答 Yes，同時說明計畫書放置的位置，故為適當的答覆。

字彙 reschedule 重新安排……的時間

5

<u>Aren't you traveling</u> to Mongolia at the end of this month?
(A) I prefer an aisle seat.
(B) No, not until next October.
(C) <u>Through</u> a travel agency.

你這個月底不是要去蒙古旅行嗎？
(A) 我比較想要靠走道的位子。
(B) 沒有，明年 10 月才去。
(C) 透過旅行社。

解析

(B) 先否定，表示這個月底沒有要去旅行，接著補充要等到明年 10 月再去，故為正確答案。(A) 使用「aisle seat」（靠走道的座位），與題目中的 travel（旅行）有所關聯，意圖使人產生混淆。

字彙 aisle seat 靠走道的座位　　not until 直到……
　　　 through 透過　　travel agency 旅行社

6

Ms. Kelly will <u>reserve the meeting room</u>, won't she?
(A) Yes, she said she'd do that.
(B) When did <u>she book it?</u>
(C) Her office is <u>upstairs</u>.

凱利女士會預約會議室，不是嗎？
(A) 是的，她說她會預約。
(B) 她何時預約的？
(C) 她的辦公室在樓上。

解析

本題詢問 Ms. Kelly（凱利女士）是否會預約會議室。(A) 表示她說她會去做，故為正確答案。(B) 使用 book，同為「預約、預訂」之意；(C) 使用單字 office（辦公室），與「meeting room」（會議室）有所關聯；兩個選項都意圖使人產生混淆。

字彙 reserve 預約、預訂　book 預約、預訂
　　　upstairs 在樓上、往樓上

7

Isn't there a job opening on the accounting team?
(A) You are welcome to apply.
(B) The shop is closed right now.
(C) The figures are a little off.

會計團隊不是有個職缺嗎？
(A) 歡迎你來應徵。
(B) 商店現在打烊了。
(C) 這些數字有點出入。

解析

本題詢問是否有職缺。(A) 表示歡迎對方應徵，為適當的答覆。(B) 使用 closed（打烊），為題目當中 opening（「職缺」，也可以解釋為「開店」）的反義詞，意圖使人產生混淆；(C) 使用 figures（數字），與「accounting team」（會計團隊）有所關聯，屬於陷阱選項。

字彙 job opening 職缺
　　　accounting team 會計團隊
　　　figure 數字、金額　off 偏離的

8

You liked the last candidate we interviewed today, didn't you?
(A) He is the right person for the job.
(B) The job interview has been delayed.
(C) We will hire only one candidate.

你很喜歡我們今天面試的最後一位應徵者，不是嗎？
(A) 他是這個工作的合適人選。
(B) 工作面試延遲了。
(C) 我們只會僱用一位應徵者。

解析

本題針對某位應徵者提出問題。(A) 表示他適任這份工作，為最適當的答覆。(C) 僅重複使用題目中的 candidate（候選人、應徵者），意圖使人產生混淆。

字彙 candidate 候選人、應徵者
　　　delay 延誤、延遲　hire 僱用

9

Isn't the art exhibition supposed to be on June 17?
(A) I was deeply impressed with that.
(B) It has been postponed.
(C) No, for twenty days.

美術展不是應該在 6 月 17 日嗎？
(A) 那讓我非常印象深刻。
(B) 展覽延期了。
(C) 不是，是 20 天。

解析

本題詢問美術展的時間。(B) 回答「延期」，故為正確答案。

字彙 art exhibition 美術展
　　　be supposed to（被認為）應該……
　　　deeply 深刻地
　　　impress 給……極深的印象
　　　postpone 延後、延期

10

You enlarged the text size, didn't you?
(A) Yes, it was too small.
(B) No, the room is big.
(C) The printer is not working.

你把內文的字級放大了，不是嗎？
(A) 是的，原來的太小了。
(B) 不，房間很大。
(C) 印表機故障了。

解析

本題詢問是否有將字體放大。(A) 表示肯定，並說明原因，故為正確答案。(B) 使用 big（大的），與題目中的 size（大小）有所關聯，但並非答案；(C) 聽到「text size」（字級大小），可能會聯想到 printer（印表機），屬於陷阱選項。

字彙 enlarge 放大、擴大

08 表示建議的問句／表示要求的問句　p.71

表示建議的問句

STEP 1 題型演練

1 (A)　2 (A)　3 (B)　4 (B)　5 (A)

1

取消下一次的董事會會議如何？
(A) 我覺得那不是個好主意。
(B) 是我們安排的。

2

我們何不打電話找技術人員？
(A) 聽起來不錯。
(B) 不是我做的。

3

你何不把結果列印出來？
(A) 週一截止。
(B) 抱歉，但是印表機故障了。

4

要不要我順便把它送去你辦公室？
(A) 我不想這樣做。
(B) 我會很感謝。

5

你想稍微休息一下嗎？
(A) 我不想這樣做。
(B) 它故障了。

STEP 3 聽寫練習

1 (A) (B)	2 (A)	3 (A) (C)
4 (A) (B)	5 (A)	6 (A)

1

Why don't we have some snacks delivered?
(A) Great. I am hungry.
(B) I think we had better.
(C) Yes, I heard it was good.

我們何不叫人送些點心來？
(A) 太好了，我餓了。
(B) 我想我們最好這麼做。
(C) 是的，我聽說那很棒。

解析

本題建議叫點心外送。(A) 和 (B) 皆表示同意此建議，故為正確答案。(C) 回答 Yes，不適用於 WH 問句，因此不適合作為答案。

字彙 snack 點心、零食
had better 最好（做）……

2

How about preparing a training session for the new employees?
(A) You bet.
(B) I am sorry, but no more hiring.
(C) I didn't like it.

為新進員工籌備一個訓練課程如何？
(A) 當然好。
(B) 抱歉，但是我們不再聘人了。
(C) 我不喜歡。

解析

本題詢問要不要為新進員工準備訓練課程。(A) 表示同意，故為正確答案。「you bet」表示「當然好」的意思，可與「of course」或「certainly」替換使用。

3

Would you like me to bring some brochures?
(A) I already got one.
(B) You'd better take a look at it.
(C) That will be great.

要不要我拿一些小冊子來？
(A) 我已經拿到一本了。
(B) 你最好看一看。
(C) 如果可以就太好了。

解析

本題詢問要不要拿手冊來。(A) 表示已經拿到了、(C) 表示同意，皆為正確答案。(A) 當中的 one 指的是「a brochure」。

字彙 brochure 小冊子、資料手冊
take a look at 看一看……

4

Why don't you move these cabinets to the corner?
(A) I'd rather not.
(B) That's a good idea.
(C) We'd better call a technician.

你何不把這些櫥櫃移到角落去？
(A) 我不想這樣做。
(B) 那是個好主意。
(C) 我們最好打電話找技術人員。

解析

本題建議將櫃子移到角落。(A) 表示不同意這個建議、(B) 則表示同意，皆為正確答案。(C) 的內容答非所問。

5

Would you like to hire more sales representatives to promote sales?

(A) I'd love to, but we can't afford to do it.
(B) Okay, I've heard about it.
(C) I didn't need one.

你想要多僱用一些業務代表來提升業績嗎?
(A) 我很想,但我們負擔不起。
(B) 好,我聽說過。
(C) 我不需要。

解析

本題詢問要不要僱用更多的業務代表。(A) 表示雖然很想,但無法負擔請人的費用,故為正確答案。afford 的意思為「有足夠的時間、(金錢上)負擔得起」。

字彙 sales representative 業務代表

6

Would you like me to pick up your lunch while I am gone?

(A) That would be wonderful.
(B) You didn't have to.
(C) We should do it.

要不要我出去的時候順便幫你買午餐?
(A) 如果可以就太好了。
(B) 你不需要這麼做的。
(C) 我們應該這麼做。

解析

本題詢問要不要在外出時順便幫對方買午餐。(A) 表示同意這個建議,故為正確答案。(B) 使用過去式,因此不適合作為答案。

表示要求的問句

STEP 1 題型演練

1 (A)   2 (B)   3 (B)   4 (B)   5 (A)

1

我可以要一張介紹這個地區的傳單嗎?
(A) 當然好,來,給你。
(B) 我們的預算沒錢了。

2

你可以幫我一起搬這張桌子嗎?
(A) 我很好,謝謝。
(B) 好啊,你想要我什麼時候幫你?

3

你介意把聲音關小一點嗎?
(A) 這音樂不太好聽。
(B) 抱歉,我不知道聲音太大了。

4

你可以把這個送去辦公室嗎?
(A) 不,我已經完成了。
(B) 好的,我正要去那裡。

5

你介意我今天提早一點離開嗎?
(A) 當然不介意。
(B) 這不關我的事。

STEP 3 聽寫練習

1 (C)   2 (A) (B)   3 (B)
4 (A)   5 (B) (C)   6 (A)

1

Could you please fill out this application form?
(A) The job is not available.
(B) I will apply for the job.
(C) I've already done it.

可以請您填寫這份申請表嗎?
(A) 沒有職缺了。
(B) 我要應徵這份工作。
(C) 我已經填過了。

解析

本題提出填寫申請表的要求。(C) 表示已經填寫完畢,故為正確答案。(A) 表示該職位已經找到人了。聽到題目中的「application form」(申請表),有可能會誤選該選項;(B) 表示要應徵該工作,此內容同樣意圖使人產生混淆。

字彙 fill out 填寫(表格、申請表等)
application form 申請表
available 可得到的

2

Do you mind changing the training schedule?
(A) Of course not. When is good for you?
(B) I don't think that's possible.
(C) It's time to learn something new.

你介意更改訓練時程嗎?
(A) 當然不介意,你何時方便?
(B) 我覺得那不可能。
(C) 該是學點新東西的時候了。

解析

本題詢問能否更動訓練時程。(A) 表示當然沒問題，並反問何時方便、(B) 則表示不太可能更動，皆為正確答案。

3

Would you call a taxi to take me to the airport?
(A) No, thanks. I will do it myself.
(B) Sure. When do you need it?
(C) The traffic was unreal.

你可以打電話叫計程車送我去機場嗎？
(A) 不用，謝謝。我可以自己來。
(B) 好。你何時需要搭車？
(C) 交通狀況很糟。

解析

本題提出請對方幫忙叫車到機場的要求。(B) 表示同意此要求，故為正確答案。(A) 不適合用來回應此要求；(C) 提及交通狀況，也不適合作為答案。

字彙 **unreal** 不真實的、無法相信的

4

Do you think you could help me with this financial report?
(A) I am busy with other things.
(B) Sorry. I don't know that.
(C) I don't believe it.

你想你可以協助我做這份財務報告嗎？
(A) 我有其他事要忙。
(B) 抱歉，我不知道那件事。
(C) 我不相信。

解析

本題提出請對方幫忙做財務報告的要求。(A) 回答正在忙著做其他工作，表示拒絕，故為正確答案。

字彙 **financial** 財務的、金融的

5

Could you help me find the M&A file?
(A) I am good. No, thanks.
(B) I have no idea where it is.
(C) I think I saw it in the drawer.

你可以幫我一起找併購的檔案嗎？
(A) 我這樣就夠了。不用了，謝謝。
(B) 我不知道它在哪裡。
(C) 我想我有看到它在抽屜裡。

解析

本題提出請對方幫忙找檔案的要求。(B) 表示自己不知道檔案在哪，可視為聽到此問題的第一反應、(C) 表示看到文件放在抽屜裡，皆為正確答案。(A) 表示拒絕，但不適合用來回答該要求。

字彙 **I'm good** 不用了、我這樣就夠了
drawer 抽屜

6

Would you mind turning off the air conditioner?
(A) Actually, I do. It's hot in here.
(B) I don't think so.
(C) They will probably like it.

你介意關掉冷氣嗎？
(A) 其實我不希望關掉，這裡很熱。
(B) 我想不是。
(C) 他們很有可能會喜歡。

解析

針對關掉冷氣的要求，(A) 表示很熱，不同意此要求，故為正確答案。mind 的意思為「介意」，因此針對用「Do you mind . . . ?」或「Would you mind . . . ?」提出的要求，回答「No, I don't.」表示同意，而回答「Yes, I do.」則是表示不同意。

字彙 **mind** 介意　　**turn off** 關掉（電器）

實戰演練 p.75

1 (A)	2 (A)	3 (B)	4 (C)	5 (B)
6 (C)	7 (C)	8 (B)	9 (B)	10 (A)

1

Would you please copy the results of the survey for the manager?
(A) I will do it after the meeting.
(B) The copy machine is working fine.
(C) Same here.

可以請你幫經理影印調查結果嗎？
(A) 開完會後我就去印。
(B) 影印機運作正常。
(C) 我也一樣。

解析

本題提出影印調查結果的要求。(A) 表示會議結束後就去印，故為正確答案。(B) 故意使用「copy machine」（影印機），意圖使人產生混淆；(C) 的內容答非所問。

字彙 copy 影印　survey 調查

same here 我也一樣、我同意

2

Could you please hand these documents over to Mr. Brown?

(A) Sure. I am available.

(B) It's my mistake.

(C) I could do with a hand.

可以請你把這些文件交給布朗先生嗎？

(A) 好，我現在有空。

(B) 是我的錯。

(C) 我需要幫忙。

解析

針對將文件轉交給 Mr. Brown（布朗先生）的要求，(A) 表示現在有空，代表會幫忙轉交，故為正確答案。

字彙 a hand 幫助、幫忙

3

Why don't we take a break before going over this report?

(A) So far, so good.

(B) Sounds like a great idea.

(C) Nothing has been broken.

我們何不休息一下，再仔細看這份報告？

(A) 目前為止，一切都順利。

(B) 聽起來是個很好的主意。

(C) 沒有打破任何東西。

解析

針對看報告前先稍作休息的要求，(B) 表示是個好主意，故為正確答案。(C) broken 表示「被打破的」，而題目中的 break 意思為「休息」。

4

How about stopping at the gas station before we head for the airport?

(A) Fill up the tank, please.

(B) I will get one for you.

(C) I think we just passed it.

在我們去機場之前，先在加油站停一下如何？

(A) 請把油箱加滿。

(B) 我會幫你拿一個。

(C) 我覺得我們剛剛經過加油站了。

解析

針對去機場前先去一下加油站的要求，(C) 表示剛剛有經過加油站，暗示應該去那一間，故為正確答案。(A) 為加油時會使用的句子；(B) 的內容答非所問。

字彙 gas station 加油站

head for 向（特定方向）出發

5

Could you take a look at my computer before you leave?

(A) Sorry. It's empty.

(B) I will try, but I can't guarantee anything.

(C) I can't find my computer.

在你離開之前，可以看一下我的電腦嗎？

(A) 抱歉，是空的。

(B) 我可以試試看，但我不能保證什麼。

(C) 我找不到我的電腦。

解析

針對離開前幫忙檢查一下電腦的要求，(B) 表示願意試試看，故為正確答案。(A) 使用單字 empty（空的），與題目中的 leave（離開）有所關聯，屬於陷阱選項；(C) 僅重複使用 computer（電腦），但並非答案。

字彙 empty 空的　guarantee 保證

6

Do you think you could give me a pay raise?

(A) Sure. I would appreciate it.

(B) He raised me up.

(C) Sorry. Not this year.

你覺得你可以幫我加薪嗎？

(A) 好，我會很感謝。

(B) 他鼓舞了我。

(C) 抱歉，今年不行。

解析

針對加薪的要求，(C) 回答今年沒辦法，表示拒絕，故為正確答案。(B) 當中的「raise up」表示「鼓舞」之意，僅重複使用題目中的 raise（加薪）一字，意圖使人產生混淆。

字彙 pay raise 加薪　appreciate 感謝

7

Why don't we reschedule Jack's retirement party for next week?

(A) Because I didn't plan it.

(B) I will be retiring soon.

(C) Let me think about it.

我們何不把傑克退休歡送會的時間改到下週？
(A) 因為我本來並不打算這麼做。
(B) 我很快就要退休了。
(C) 讓我想一想。

解析

針對將 Jack（傑克）的退休歡送會改到下週的要求，(C) 表示要考慮一下，故為正確答案。(A) 的內容答非所問；(B) 僅重複使用 retire（退休），但並非答案。

8

Why don't you take a few days off and relax?
(A) I didn't turn it off.
(B) I'd love to.
(C) The best vacation ever.

你何不休幾天假，放鬆一下？
(A) 我沒有把它關掉。
(B) 我非常想這麼做。
(C) 是目前為止最棒的假期。

解析

針對休假幾天的建議，(B) 表示願意，故為正確答案。(A) 使用「turn off」（關掉），僅與題目中的「take off」（休假）發音相近，意圖使人產生混淆；(C) 故意使用 vacation（假期），僅與「day off」（休假）的意思相近，但並非答案。

9

Do you mind helping me with the inventory?
(A) I don't mind working long hours.
(B) Of course not.
(C) Sure. I can do that.

你介意幫我盤點存貨嗎？
(A) 我不介意長時間工作。
(B) 當然不介意。
(C) 當然介意，我可以做。

解析

針對幫忙盤點庫存的要求，(B) 表示願意幫忙，故為正確答案。題目句開頭為「Do you mind . . .」，因此要用否定句來表示同意要求，如選項 (B) 的「of course not」。而 (C) 回答 sure（當然），表示拒絕，與後方的語意不合。

字彙 mind 介意　inventory 存貨、存貨盤點

10

Would you like to give a speech at the opening ceremony?
(A) Sorry, but I will pass this time.
(B) He is such a good speaker.
(C) Not at all.

你想要在開幕典禮上演說嗎？
(A) 抱歉，但我這次就不要了。
(B) 他是非常棒的一位講者。
(C) 一點也不。

解析

本題詢問是否願意在開幕典禮上演講。(A) 表示這次不想，故為正確答案。pass 有很多意思，在該選項中表示「跳過、略過」之意。注意 (C) 雖然表示否定，但通常是用來回應「Do/Would you mind . . . ?」（你介意……嗎？）句型，表示不介意，因此並不適合作為答案。

字彙 opening ceremony 開幕典禮
　　　 not at all 一點也不

09 直述句　　　　　　　　　p.77

提出問題點

STEP 1 題型演練

| 1 (B) | 2 (A) | 3 (A) | 4 (B) | 5 (A) |

1

我們的車快沒油了。
(A) 我的車故障了。
(B) 最近的加油站在哪裡？

2

我無法啟動這台投影機。
(A) 試試紅色的按鈕。
(B) 照片不清楚。

3

報告上的數字不正確。
(A) 李先生晚點會校對。
(B) 謝謝你的幫忙。

4

我的班機已經誤點八個小時了。
(A) 機場太擁擠了。
(B) 你何不試試另一班飛機？

5

我的筆電不動了。
(A) 那不是新的嗎？
(B) 事情進展如何？

STEP 3 聽寫練習

1 (B)	2 (B) (C)	3 (C)
4 (A) (B)	5 (B)	6 (A) (C)

1

The coffee maker is out of order.
(A) It might need more cups.
(B) Did you call a repairman?
(C) The shipment is delayed.

咖啡機故障了。
(A) 可能需要更多杯子。
(B) 你打電話找維修人員了嗎？
(C) 配送延誤了。

解析

本題以直述句提出咖啡機故障一事。對此，(B) 詢問是否已經聯絡維修人員，為最適當的答覆。無論是需要更多的杯子還是配送延誤，皆與題目內容無關，因此 (A) 和 (C) 皆不是答案。

字彙 out of order 故障　repairman 維修人員
shipment 貨物配送

2

I don't think I can finish the budget report today.
(A) We are short of money.
(B) Is it urgent?
(C) I'd love to help you.

我覺得我今天無法完成預算報告。
(A) 我們的錢不夠。
(B) 很趕嗎？
(C) 我很樂意幫你。

解析

本題表達無法完成報告一事。(B) 詢問報告是否很趕、(C) 表示願意幫忙，皆為正確答案。(A) 使用「short of money」（錢不夠），僅與 budget（預算）有所關聯，但並非答案。

字彙 short of 缺少……的　urgent 緊急的、急迫的

3

I didn't realize that the pharmacy was closed today.
(A) Dr. Wilson is on vacation.
(B) You'd better see a doctor.
(C) The one on Maple Street is open.

我不知道藥局今天休息。
(A) 威爾森先生去度假了。
(B) 你最好去看醫生。
(C) 楓樹街上那家有開。

解析

本題表達不知道藥局今天沒有營業。(C) 告知對方哪裡的藥局有營業，故為正確答案。

字彙 pharmacy 藥局

4

I can't find the confidential personnel files.
(A) Nancy was looking at them yesterday.
(B) Have you looked into the safe?
(C) The key is missing.

我找不到機密人事檔案。
(A) 南西昨天在看。
(B) 你找過保險箱了嗎？
(C) 鑰匙不見了。

解析

本題提出找不到檔案的問題。對此，(A) 表示 Nancy（南西）昨天有看那些檔案、(B) 詢問是否有找過保險箱，皆為正確答案。(C) 鑰匙不見與找不到檔案沒有直接關係，因此不適合作為答案。

字彙 confidential 機密的　personnel 人事
safe 保險箱

5

This product brochure is outdated.
(A) Let's go outside.
(B) The marketing team is updating it.
(C) I like the design.

這份產品手冊過時了。
(A) 我們到外面去。
(B) 行銷團隊正在將它更新。
(C) 我喜歡這個設計。

解析

本題提到產品手冊的內容過時。對此，(B) 表示目前正在更新，故為正確答案。

6

The photocopier has a paper jam again.
(A) I think we need a better one.
(B) The report is on your desk.
(C) Do you want me to take a look?

影印機又卡紙了。
(A) 我覺得我們需要一台比較好的。
(B) 報告在你桌上。
(C) 要不要我來看一下？

解析

本題提出影印機的問題。對此，(A) 建議換一台更好的影印機、(C) 詢問是否需要幫助，皆為正確答案。

表達消息或意見

STEP 1 題型演練

1 (B)　2 (A)　3 (A)　4 (B)　5 (B)

1

整修工作將從 6 月開始。
(A) 正在興建中。
(B) 不是 5 月就該開始了嗎？

2

我打來是想取消我的義大利之旅。
(A) 您要重新安排時間嗎？
(B) 他正在度假。

3

你應該去散個步，而不是待在屋裡。
(A) 是的，我需要一些新鮮空氣。
(B) 我今天上班遲到了。

4

軟體已升級成新的版本。
(A) 幾天前。
(B) 那不是很棒嗎？

5

我今天稍晚會預訂飯店房間和機票。
(A) 真的很好玩。
(B) 你要去哪裡？

STEP 3 聽寫練習

1 (B)　　　2 (A) (B)　　3 (A) (C)
4 (B) (C)　　5 (B)　　　6 (A) (C)

1

I think Mr. Harris is the perfect candidate for the project.
(A) My interview went well.
(B) Yes, he is reliable.
(C) Only two candidates.

我認為哈里斯先生是這個專案的最佳人選。
(A) 我的面試很順利。
(B) 是的，他很可靠。
(C) 只有兩位候選人。

解析

本題提出認為 Mr. Harris（哈里斯先生）為適任的人選。對此，(B) 表示同意這個看法，故為正確答案。(A) 故意提及 interview（面試），意圖使人產生混淆；(C) 僅重複使用 candidate（候選人、應徵者），但並非答案。

字彙 candidate 候選人、應徵者　interview 面試

2

You should put on a protective helmet at the construction site.
(A) Where can I get one?
(B) Then I have to borrow one.
(C) I am wearing a hat.

你在建築工地應該要戴上安全帽。
(A) 我要去哪裡拿？
(B) 那麼我必須借一頂來。
(C) 我戴著帽子。

解析

本題提出在工地應戴上安全帽。(A) 詢問取得安全帽的地方、(B) 表示要借一頂安全帽，皆為正確答案。(C) 當中的 hat（帽子）指的並非安全帽，因此不適合作為答案。

字彙 put on 穿上、戴上（衣物）
protective helmet 安全帽
construction site 建築工地

3

I put your mail on your desk.
(A) Thanks. I will check it later.
(B) I hope it arrives soon.
(C) I didn't see anything.

我把你的信放在你桌上。
(A) 謝謝，我晚點再看。
(B) 我希望它快點到。
(C) 我什麼也沒看到。

解析

本題表示將信放在對方桌上。(A) 表達感謝之意、(C) 表示沒有看到信，皆為正確答案。

4

I heard that we are all getting a bonus at the end of this month.
(A) I am looking for the bank.
(B) I didn't expect that.
(C) Do you know how much it will be?

我聽說，我們全部人這個月底都會有獎金。
(A) 我正在找銀行。
(B) 我沒想到會有。
(C) 你知道會有多少嗎？

解析

本題表示聽說會拿到獎金的消息。(B) 表示對此並未感到期待、(C) 詢問確切的金額為多少，皆為適當的答覆。

字彙 look for 尋找

5

The quarterly report is due this week.
(A) Sales are not bad.
(B) I thought it was last week.
(C) It was quite impressive.

季報告這週須繳交。
(A) 業績不錯。
(B) 我以為上週就要交了。
(C) 令人相當印象深刻。

解析

本題表示報告繳交的截止時間。(B) 表示截止時間為上週，並非這週，為適當的答覆。

字彙 quarterly 季的　impressive 令人印象深刻的

6

I think we should put off our office party.
(A) I agree with you.
(B) We are running late.
(C) How about next Friday then?

我認為我們應該把辦公室派對延後。
(A) 我同意。
(B) 我們快來不及了。
(C) 那（延到）下週五如何？

解析

本題表示應延後辦公室派對。(A) 對此表示同意、(C) 提出替代方案，皆為正確答案。

字彙 put off 延後、拖延

實戰演練　p.81

1 (A)	2 (B)	3 (A)	4 (B)	5 (C)
6 (A)	7 (C)	8 (C)	9 (C)	10 (B)

1

These new computers are so much faster.
(A) They really are.
(B) Sorry. I already had some.
(C) We should update the software.

這些新電腦快多了。
(A) 它們真的很快。
(B) 抱歉，我已經有一些了。
(C) 我們應該將軟體升級。

解析

本題表示電腦速度很快。(A) 對此表示同意，故為正確答案。(B) 和 (C) 皆為答非所問。

2

I want to take the afternoon flight to Sydney.
(A) For my brother's graduation.
(B) How about the morning one?
(C) It was a short trip.

我想搭下午飛往雪梨的航班。
(A) 為了我哥哥的畢業典禮。
(B) 那早上的航班如何？
(C) 是短程旅行。

解析

本題表示欲搭乘下午的航班。(B) 提出其他方案，故為正確答案。若選項使用反問法、或提出其他方案，皆適合作為答案。

字彙 graduation 畢業、畢業典禮

3

I can't get the copier to work properly.
(A) Does it need a new cartridge?
(B) The other supplier has better paper.
(C) I got to work at 10 o'clock.

影印機無法正常運作。
(A) 是不是需要新的墨水匣?
(B) 其他供應商有更好的紙。
(C) 我 10 點上班。

解析

本題提出影印機的問題。(A) 提出解決的方案,故為正確答案。(B) 提及紙張供應商、(C) 告知上班時間,皆與題目內容無關。

字彙 properly 正確地

4

Professor Garcia will be free on Thursday morning.
(A) I have never been here before.
(B) What about Tuesday morning?
(C) The classroom is upstairs.

賈西亞教授週四早上有空。
(A) 我以前從來沒來過這裡。
(B) 那週二早上呢?
(C) 教室在樓上。

解析

本題提出教授週四上午有空。對此,(B) 詢問其他時間可不可以,故為正確答案。

字彙 upstairs 在樓上、往樓上

5

I don't know how to use this new fax machine.
(A) I can join you.
(B) No, I have been using it well.
(C) I saw the manual somewhere.

我不知道這台新傳真機怎麼用。
(A) 我可以和你一起。
(B) 不,我一直都用得很順。
(C) 我在某個地方有看到使用手冊。

解析

本題表示不知道機器的使用方法。(C) 提到曾看過使用手冊,為適當的答覆。(B) 僅重複使用 use(使用),但並非答案。

字彙 manual 使用手冊

6

I found a new supplier for the plastic containers we use.
(A) Are the prices better?
(B) Take the inventory, please.
(C) We bought a lot of bottles.

我為我們用的塑膠容器找到一個新的供應商。
(A) 價格比較優惠嗎?
(B) 請盤點存貨。
(C) 我們買了很多瓶。

解析

本題表示找到新的供應商。(A) 反問價格是否比較優惠,故為正確答案。(B) 使用單字 inventory(存貨),僅與 supplier(供應商)有所關聯;(C) 使用 bottle(瓶),僅與 container(容器)有所關聯,兩者皆意圖使人產生混淆。

字彙 container 容器
take the inventory 盤點存貨

7

I haven't heard who was chosen as vice president.
(A) It was last Friday.
(B) Please have a seat.
(C) I believe it was Ms. White.

我還沒聽說是誰當選副總裁。
(A) 是上週五。
(B) 請坐。
(C) 我相信是懷特女士。

解析

本題表示不知道誰被選為副總裁。(C) 告知副總裁是誰,故為正確答案。(A) 告知的是選出的日期,而 (B) 的內容答非所問。

字彙 vice president 副總裁

8

I just found out that the new security system didn't work.
(A) Yes, we repaired it yesterday.
(B) It is a safe neighborhood.
(C) Did you call the maintenance team?

我剛剛發現新的保全系統故障了。
(A) 是的,我們昨天修理了。
(B) 這一區治安很好。
(C) 你打電話給維修團隊了嗎?

解析

本題提出新的保全系統發生故障。(C) 詢問是否有通知維修團隊,故為正確答案。(A) 表示昨天修理過,但題目是指現在發現故障一事,因此不適合作為答案;(B) 故意使用「safe neighborhood」(附近治安好),僅與 security(保全)有所關聯,屬於陷阱選項。

字彙 security 保全　neighborhood 鄰近地區
maintenance team 維修團隊

9

I'd like to <u>fill this prescription</u>, please.
(A) No worries.
(B) I <u>took the medication</u>.
(C) When do you want to pick it up?

我要照這個處方箋配藥，謝謝。
(A) 別擔心。
(B) 我吃過藥了。
(C) 你想要何時來拿？

解析

該對話發生在藥局。本題提出按照處方箋配藥的要求，(C) 詢問對方希望領藥的時間，故為正確答案。

字彙 **fill this prescription** 照這個處方箋配藥
medication 藥物、藥物治療
pick up 拿取

10

We <u>have to cancel</u> the outdoor concert.
(A) A rock music festival.
(B) I think it is too late.
(C) Yes, I <u>would love to go</u>.

我們必須取消戶外音樂會。
(A) 一場搖滾音樂節。
(B) 我覺得來不及取消了。
(C) 是的，我很想去。

解析

本題表示要取消演唱會。(B) 回答「I think it is too late」，表示現在取消太晚了，故為正確答案。

多益實戰單字 PART 2 UNIT 06 - 09　　　p.83

A
1 (A)　**2** (B)　**3** (A)　**4** (A)　**5** (B)

B
1 due　　　　**2** held
3 confidential　**4** in cash
5 candidate

C
1 are going to get a bonus
2 happen to know what he does
3 want me to go with you
4 Aren't you supposed to
5 like me to take you

PART **3** 簡短對話 Short Conversations

01 會議／活動　　　　p.86

STEP 1 題型演練

1 (A)　　　**2** (B)

1
談話的人主要在談什麼？
(A) 新網頁
(B) 行銷策略
(C) 產品缺陷

解析

對話開頭處，女子提到要討論網頁的新設計一事（Let's start today's meeting by discussing the new web page redesign），因此答案為 (A)。

2
談話的人正在討論什麼問題？
(A) 資金不足
(B) 和公司商標不搭
(C) 新商標的設計不佳

解析

對話中提到原來的公司商標與新網站不搭（Our old logo looks kind of bad on the new website），因此答案為 (B)。

STEP 2 常考用法

1 call off this meeting
2 I think we should
3 convention center / host the events
4 attend the seminar / sign up for
5 come up with / promote sales
6 go over today's agenda

STEP 3 聽寫練習

1 (D)　　　**2** (B)

1

M Well, I think that's all we need to take care of today. Do you have any other questions?

W I don't think so. Oh, actually, there is one thing. I want to know when the Frederick Building project will be finished.

M That's hard to say. We've had some problems getting a few required construction permits, so there have been some major delays.

W I see. Well, if you get a more certain timeline for the project, please let me know.

男 嗯，我想我們今天該處理的都全談完了。你還有其他問題嗎？

女 我想沒有了。噢，其實還有一件事，我想知道弗雷德里克大樓的建案什麼時候會完成。

男 這很難說。我們在取得所需的幾張建築執照時出了點狀況，所以進度嚴重落後。

女 了解。好，如果你有更明確的時程，請再跟我說。

男子說「這很難說」，意思可能為何？
(A) 此為機密資訊。
(B) 他不想告訴女子。
(C) 他將以電子郵件通知女子。
(D) 他目前還不確定。

解析

男子說出該句話後提到「在取得所需的幾張建築執照時出了點狀況，所以進度嚴重落後」（We've had some problems getting a few required construction permits, so there have been some major delays），表示他還無法確定建案何時能完成，因此答案為 (D)。

2

M So, Sharon, did you get the results of the survey about the venue for the end-of-the-year party?

W I did. Here are the results. Contrary to our expectations, Paradise Palms got the most votes.

M But do you know what? I just got a call from them, and they said they are fully booked on the day of our party.

W Oh, no. Our employees really want that place. What should we do?

M We should probably have the party at the second-most popular place.

W Yeah, I think so. I will call them and make a reservation before the end of the day.

男 所以雪倫，你收到年終派對場地調查的結果了嗎？

女 我收到了，結果在這裡。和我們預期的相反，樂園棕櫚得到最高票。

男 但你知道嗎？我剛接到他們的電話，說我們派對當天的預約已經滿了。

女 噢，不。我們員工真的很想要那個場地，我們該怎麼辦才好？

男 或許我們應該把派對辦在第二高票的場地。

女 對，我也這麼想。我下班前會打電話過去預約。

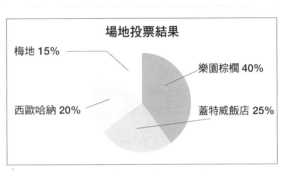

場地投票結果

梅地 15%
樂園棕櫚 40%
西歐哈納 20%
蓋特威飯店 25%

請看圖表。談話的人有可能會在哪裡辦活動？
(A) 樂園棕櫚
(B) 蓋特威飯店
(C) 西歐哈納
(D) 梅地

解析

對話中提到員工最想要的場地為 Paradise Palms（樂園棕櫚），但是已經被訂走了，因此建議選擇票數第二高的地方舉辦派對（We should probably have the party at the second-most popular place）。圖中顯示票數第二高的場地為 Gateway Hotel（蓋特威飯店），由此可知會在此舉辦活動。

實戰演練　　　　p.89

1 (B)	2 (A)	3 (C)
4 (B)	5 (D)	6 (A)

[1-3]

M1 Let's get started. The first thing we need to discuss is our decrease in cell phone accessory sales. Does anyone have any ideas?

M2 I think we can improve sales if we have more packages that include accessories when you buy a new phone.

W You have a point there. Right now, the packages are really limited, and most customers aren't interested in them. I think we need more options for them.

M1 I like that idea. Suki, can you work with the sales team to come up with some new package ideas?

W Sure. I will prepare some sample packages that we can discuss at next week's meeting.

男1 我們開始吧。首先要討論的,是手機配件的銷售量下滑這件事。有沒有人有任何想法?

男2 我覺得購買新手機時,如果有更多搭配配件的組合方案可以選,銷售量就能提升。

女 你說的有道理。現在的組合方案真的很有限,大多數的消費者根本沒興趣。我覺得我們應該要給他們更多選擇。

男1 我也覺得這想法不錯。壽紀,你能和銷售團隊一起發想幾個新方案的點子嗎?

女 好啊。我也會準備幾個暫定的組合方案,我們下週開會可以討論。

字彙 **decrease** 減少　**improve** 提高
limited 有限的
come up with 想出(點子、方案等)

1

這間公司碰到什麼問題?

(A) 手機配件不足。

(B) 賣出的手機配件不夠多。

(C) 顧客不滿其現有的購機方案。

(D) 沒人想販售手機配件。

解析

對話開頭處提到,首先要討論的是手機配件銷售量下滑一事(decrease in cell phone accessory sales),代表銷售量未達公司預期賣出的數量,因此答案為 (B)。

2

女子說「你說的有道理」,意思可能為何?

(A) 她同意男子的意見。

(B) 她對於該建議的好壞不是很確定。

(C) 這些男子應該對該點子再三思量。

(D) 這些男子應該從頭來過。

解析

男子提出自己的想法,表示如果增加更多搭配配件的組合方案,便能改善銷售量(we can improve sales if we have more packages that include accessories when you buy a new phone)。而後女子表示此話很有道理(You have a point there),也就是同意男子的說法,因此答案為 (A)。

3

女子說她會做什麼?

(A) 販售更多手機配件

(B) 研究最新的手機型號

(C) 發想配件組合方案的新點子

(D) 移動到賣場樓層

解析

後半段對話中,女子提到會準備幾個暫定的組合方案(I will prepare some sample packages),因此答案為 (C)。

[4-6]

W Thanks for making time to meet with me today. We have so much to do to prepare before the new professor arrives.

M Of course. Have you found an office for him to use yet?

W Yes, there is a space available in the humanities building, so I will finish the preparations this week. But we still need someone to pick him up from the airport when he arrives. Do you think Dr. Hall can do it?

M I'm not sure, but I can ask her. Could you email me his flight details?

W Sure, I'll send them right over. When can you talk with Dr. Hall?

M Actually, let me give her a ring right now.

女 感謝你空出時間跟我開會。在新教授來之前,我們有很多事要準備。

男 當然。你找到辦公室給他用了嗎?

女 有，人文大樓有空房間，我這週就能搞定。但他到機場的時候，我們還需要有人接機。你覺得霍爾博士可以幫忙嗎？

男 我不確定，但我會問問她。可以請你寄他的班機資訊給我嗎？

女 好，我馬上寄。你什麼時候能和霍爾博士講？

男 我現在就立刻打電話給她。

4

談話的人最有可能在哪裡工作？

(A) 門市樓層
(B) 大學
(C) 建設公司
(D) 飯店

解析

聽到「new professor」（新教授）、「office」（辦公室）、「Dr. Hall」（霍爾博士）等單字，便能推測出說話者在大學裡面工作，因此答案為 (B)。

5

談話的人主要在討論什麼？

(A) 他們下次會議的時程安排
(B) 工作場所政策異動
(C) 辦公室整修
(D) 新應聘的系所成員

解析

女子提到新教授來之前，有很多事得準備（We have so much to do to prepare before the new professor arrives），新教授應為系上新聘的成員，因此答案為 (D)。

6

男子接著最有可能做什麼？

(A) 打電話給霍爾博士
(B) 用電子郵件寄他的班機資訊
(C) 聯絡新教授
(D) 準備新辦公室

解析

後半段對話中，女子詢問男子什麼時候可以跟霍爾博士講。男子表示現在馬上打電話（let me give her a ring right now），由此可知男子要做的事為 (A)。

---

02 業務／日程

p.91

STEP 1 題型演練

> **1** (B)　　　**2** (A)

1

晚餐將在哪裡吃？

(A) 義大利餐廳
(B) 印度餐廳
(C) 中餐廳

解析

第一段對話中，女子提到她訂了印度餐廳（I booked a table at the Indian restaurant down the road），因此答案為 (B)。

2

女子接下來會做什麼？

(A) 她會寄電子郵件給男子。
(B) 她將聯絡霍克先生。
(C) 她會訂位。

解析

當題目詢問接下來要做的事情時，請務必專心聽清楚最後一段對話的內容。後半段對話中，男子要求女子用電子郵件寄訂位資訊給他（Can you email me the reservation details when you have a moment?），而後女子回答「當然沒問題」（Of course），因此答案為 (A)。

STEP 2 常考用法

1 want to have a day off / have to get approval
2 get an extension on the budget report
3 put off the company banquet
4 calling about the reimbursement
5 call off the outdoor event scheduled
6 reviewing the safety records

STEP 3 聽寫練習

> **1** (C)　　　**2** (D)

1

W Hey, Jim, have you <u>seen the quarterly reports</u> from the Marketing Department yet? They told me they would be ready by today, but I <u>haven't heard from them</u>.

M No, I haven't heard anything either. Maybe they are <u>running behind</u> schedule. I know they are busy this time of year. Do you want me to <u>give them a call</u>?

W That's all right. I'm <u>going downstairs</u> now, so I'll just <u>stop by</u>. Do you need anything else from them?

M I don't think so. Thanks anyway.

女 嗨,吉姆,你看到行銷部的季報告了嗎?他們跟我說今天會做好,但到現在還沒有消息。

男 沒有耶,我也沒聽說,也許他們進度落後了吧。我知道每年的這個時候他們都很忙。要不要我打個電話給他們?

女 沒關係。我正要下樓,所以我會順路過去看看。你有其他東西需要跟他們拿嗎?

男 應該是沒有。不管怎樣,謝啦。

女子接下來最有可能做什麼?
(A) 打電話給行銷部
(B) 撰寫季報告
(C) 拜訪行銷部
(D) 協助吉姆工作

解析

女子提到下樓時會順道過去一趟(I'm going downstairs now, so I'll just stop by),表示她要去行銷部,因此答案為 (C)。

2

M Ms. Carter, I wonder if I can <u>have next Monday off</u>. Do you think that would be possible?

W Next Monday? Yeah, I think that should be okay. Did you <u>make an official request</u> on the digital scheduling system?

M Not yet. I wanted to check with you first <u>to make sure it would be okay</u>.

W Okay, well, make sure you file your request <u>by the end of the day</u> so that I can <u>approve your time off</u>.

M That sounds good. Thanks, Ms. Carter.

男 卡特女士,我想知道下週一我能不能休假。您覺得可以嗎?

女 下週一?可以啊,我認為應該沒問題。你到線上排班系統提出正式申請了嗎?

男 還沒,我想先和您確認可不可以。

女 好,那麼請你記得下班前提出申請,我才能批准你休假。

男 太好了。謝謝您,卡特女士。

女子說「我認為應該沒問題」,意思為何?
(A) 男子不須做任何額外的工作。
(B) 男子可以延後專案期限。
(C) 男子可以申請轉調。
(D) 男子可以休一天假。

解析

女子所說的話是針對男子詢問週一可否請假(I wonder if I can have next Monday off)的答覆,表示「我認為應該沒問題」,因此答案選 (D)。

實戰演練 p.94

| 1 (C) | 2 (B) | 3 (C) |
| 4 (B) | 5 (A) | 6 (B) |

[1-3]

W James, I have a client coming this afternoon <u>to discuss a small business loan</u>. He has all of his <u>business accounts with us</u>, so it's a very important meeting. Can you book Room 105 at 2 P.M. for me, please?

M Room 105? That's where the new teller training will be happening this afternoon. Do you <u>want me to look for another room</u>?

W Oh, yes, that would be great. Could you <u>check the schedule</u>?

M Yeah, it looks like <u>there is another room free</u> at 2 P.M. It's <u>the biggest room available</u> at that time. I'll <u>email you the details</u>.

W Perfect. Thank you so much.

女 詹姆斯,我今天下午有客戶要來談一筆小型企業貸款的事,他所有的公司帳戶都是在我們銀行開的,所以這次會面非常重要。你可以幫我預約下午 2 點的 105 號室嗎?

男 105 號室嗎?今天新進櫃員的教育訓練會在那裡辦耶。要不要我找找看其他地方?

女 噢，好，如果可以就太好了。你能幫我確認一下預約表嗎？

男 好，2點時有另一間會議室可以用，是那時所有可以用的會議室當中最大的。詳細資訊我再用電子郵件寄給您。

女 太棒了，感激不盡。

字彙 client 客戶　loan 貸款　account 帳戶
　　 teller 銀行櫃員　detail 詳細資訊

時間	會議室	座位數
下午2點	105	8
	106	10
	107	12
	108	6

1

談話的人在討論什麼？
(A) 貸款給顧客
(B) 開戶
(C) 預約會議室
(D) 聯絡企業客戶

解析

雖然對話中有提 loan（貸款）和 account（帳戶），但是主要在討論的是預約會議室一事，因此答案為(C) Reserving a conference room。

2

男子說他會做什麼？
(A) 取消會議
(B) 寄會議室資訊給女子
(C) 一起開會
(D) 訓練新進櫃員

解析

男子提到會把詳細內容用電子郵件寄給女子（I'll email you the details），因此答案選 (B) Send the woman the room information。

3

請看圖表。女子將在哪裡與客戶會面？
(A) 105 號室
(B) 106 號室
(C) 107 號室
(D) 108 號室

解析

男子提到該會議室是那個時段空出的會議室中最大間的（It's the biggest room available at that time），查看表格後，會發現 107 號室可以容納 12 人，容納人數最多，因此答案為 (C)。

[4-6]

W Hi, Hans. I reviewed the trip you planned for Globi Technology. You did an excellent job.

M Thanks. I really enjoyed working with them on their travel plans.

W How would you feel about becoming our newest team leader? I think that you would do a wonderful job managing your own group of agents.

M Wow, do you really think so? I don't know what to say. That would be an amazing opportunity for me.

W Well, think about it over the weekend, and we can discuss the details next Monday.

女 嗨，漢斯。我看了你為環球科技規劃的旅遊行程，規劃得太棒了。

男 謝謝。和他們一起排行程真的很愉快。

女 你覺得我升你當我們公司新的團隊主管怎麼樣？我認為你能把自己的組員管理得很好。

男 哇，您真的這麼覺得嗎？我不知道該說什麼。這對我來說是個很好的機會。

女 嗯嗯，你趁週末考慮一下，我們下週一再詳細討論。

字彙 review 審閱　team leader 團隊主管
　　 manage 管理　agent 旅行社職員
　　 opportunity 機會

4

談話的人最有可能在哪裡工作？
(A) 銀行
(B) 旅行社
(C) 法律事務所
(D) 搬家公司

解析

男子表示非常享受旅遊行程的規劃過程（I really enjoyed working with them on their travel plans），因此答案應為 (B) 旅行社。

5

女子提議給男子什麼？

(A) 升職
(B) 新搬公室
(C) 出國旅遊
(D) 更多休假

解析

女子詢問男子有沒有意願當新團隊的主管（How would you feel about becoming our newest team leader?），因此答案為 (A)。

6

男子說「我不知道該說什麼」，意思為何？

(A) 他很困惑。
(B) 他很驚訝。
(C) 他對該話題不熟悉。
(D) 他現在不能幫忙。

解析

女子提議將男子升職，對此男子表示「I don't know what to say」，表示他對此建議相當驚訝，因此答案選 (B)。

03 人事／聘用　　　　　　　　　p.96

STEP 1 題型演練

┌─────────────────────────┐
│ 1 (B)　　　　2 (A) │
└─────────────────────────┘

1

米娜提到什麼問題？

(A) 她忘記密碼。
(B) 她無法登入人資網站。
(C) 她無法更新自己的網站。

解析

Mina（米娜）提到她無法登入人資網站的員工頁面（I can't log into my employee page on the HR website），因此答案為 (B)。

2

莎夏最有可能在哪裡工作？

(A) 人資部
(B) 技術部
(C) 會計部

解析

為解決 Mina（米娜）無法登入人資網站員工頁面的問題，Sasha（莎夏）向她詢問員工編號（What's your employee ID number?），並將操作說明用電子郵件寄給她。Sasha（莎夏）協助解決與人資網站有關的問題，表示她是人資部的員工。

STEP 2 常考用法

1 take a day off
2 job opening
3 job fair / potential employees
4 recruit new staff
5 apply for / position / cover letter
6 renew your contract / performance evaluation

STEP 3 聽寫練習

┌─────────────────────────┐
│ 1 (B)　　　　2 (A) │
└─────────────────────────┘

1

M Have you reviewed the applicant résumés for the new programmer position? I sent them to your office last week.

W I started, but I haven't finished yet. There was a lot of interest in the position, so it's taking longer than expected.

M Yeah, I noticed that there were a lot more applications than the last time. I'm happy about the increase in popularity.

W It's great. I should be finished by the end of the week, so let's go over them together next Monday.

M Perfect. See you then.

男 你看過新程式設計師應徵者的履歷了嗎？我上週送到你辦公室了。
女 我開始看了，但還沒有看完。有很多人對那個職位感興趣，所以比我預期的還要花時間。
男 對啊，我有注意到這次的求職者比上次多。詢問度增加我還蠻高興的。
女 很好啊。我應該會在週末放假前看完，我們下週一再一起審查。
男 太棒了，那就到時見囉。

下週一將發生什麼事？
(A) 他們將聘用新員工。
(B) 談話的人將一起看履歷。
(C) 女子將寄履歷給男子。
(D) 談話的人將聯絡招聘對象。

解析

後半段對話中，女子提到下週一再一起審查（let's go over them together next Monday），因此答案為 (B)。

2

W What time will the new interns arrive on Monday?

M The orientation is scheduled to start at 9 A.M. Have you finished preparing their info packets yet?

W Not quite, but they will be ready by the end of the day. Do you have a final number on how many interns are coming?

M There should be 12, so make sure to print enough packets for each of them.

W Will do. Thanks, Barry.

女 新實習生週一什麼時候到？

男 教育訓練表定上午9點開始。你準備好要給他們的資料包了嗎？

女 還沒，但今天下班前會準備好。你知道最終會來的實習生人數嗎？

男 應該有12位，所以要確認印的資料包足夠給每個人。

女 會啦。謝囉，巴里。

談話的人最有可能在哪一個部門工作？
(A) 人資部
(B) 行銷部
(C) 會計部
(D) 產品開發部

解析

對話內容與新實習生的教育訓練有關，表示說話者應在人資部（Human Resources）工作較為合理，因此答案為 (A)。

實戰演練　　　　　　　　　　　p.99

p.99

1 (B)	2 (D)	3 (A)
4 (B)	5 (A)	6 (A)

[1-3]

M Excuse me. I'm sorry to bother you, but I think there was a mistake with my last paycheck. My commission wasn't included.

W You have to be kidding. You're the third person who has had this problem this month. Do you have your paycheck information with you?

M Oh, really? Yes, here is my info. How long should it take to correct the problem?

W Let's see. Yes, this shouldn't be a problem. I'll process it right now, and you should receive the missing money on Wednesday morning.

M Oh, that's great. Thank you so much.

男 抱歉打擾您，但我覺得我上個月的薪資單有問題，沒有算到我的傭金。

女 不是在開玩笑吧，您已經是這個月第三位反映同樣問題的人了。您有沒有把您的薪資資料帶來？

男 噢，真的嗎？有的，我的資料在這裡。這個問題要多久才能解決呢？

女 我看看噢。嗯，這不成問題。我馬上處理，您週三早上應該就會收到漏給您的錢。

男 噢，太好了。感激不盡。

字彙 bother 打擾　paycheck 薪資單
commission 傭金　correct 修正、解決
process 處理

1

男子為什麼去這間辦公室？
(A) 他把薪資單弄丟了。
(B) 他沒拿到正確的薪資。
(C) 他需要額外的錢。
(D) 他想修改一些個人資料。

解析

男子提到薪資中並未包含應得的傭金（My commission wasn't included），因此答案為 (B)。

2

女子為什麼說「不是在開玩笑吧」？
(A) 指控男子撒謊
(B) 請男子晚點再過來
(C) 叫男子停止開玩笑
(D) 表示她很驚訝

解析

女子說完這句話後，接著又提到男子已經是這個月第三位碰到相同問題的人了（You're the third person who has had this problem this month）。由此可知女子說出這句話，是表示自己對此件事感到驚訝。

3

週三將發生什麼事？

(A) 男子將拿到正確的薪資。
(B) 女子會再聯絡男子。
(C) 男子將重返該辦公室。
(D) 女子將處理男子的要求。

解析

女子表示會立刻處理男子碰到的問題，而且他在週三早上便能拿到錢（I'll process it right now, and you should receive the missing money on Wednesday morning），因此答案選 (A)。

[4-6]

M Hello. I'm interested in <u>applying for a position</u> as a web page designer, but I have a question.

W Of course. Thanks for <u>your interest in the position</u>. How can I help you?

M <u>I wonder</u> when the starting date for the position is. It says here on the website that <u>it starts on</u> July 15. I also would like to know when the <u>application deadline</u> is.

W Oh, yes, the <u>expected starting date</u> is July 20. The 15th is for programmers and the <u>floor manager</u>. And all <u>applications are due</u> by June 1. Do you have any other questions?

M No, <u>that's exactly what</u> I needed to know. Thank you.

W You're very welcome. Have a great day.

男 您好。我有意願應徵網頁設計師，但我有問題想問。

女 好的，感謝您對該職位有興趣。我有什麼能夠幫您的嗎？

男 我想知道該職位開始工作的時間；網站說是從 7 月 15 日開始。我也想問一下應徵截止日期是什麼時候。

女 噢，預計開始工作的日期是 7 月 20 日，而 15 日則是程式設計師和樓管的上工日。所有職位應徵的截止日都是 6 月 1 日。您還有其他問題嗎？

男 沒有了，這正是我想知道的。謝謝您。

女 不客氣，祝您有美好的一天。

字彙 apply for 應徵（職位） application 應徵 deadline 截止期限

職位	職缺數	部門
網頁設計師	2	網路管理
程式設計師	4	資訊發展
產品研發人員	2	研發
樓管	1	業務

4

男子為什麼打電話？

(A) 為了取消應徵
(B) **為了了解應徵程序**
(C) 為了應徵某職位
(D) 為了找到網站的網址

解析

男子詢問開始工作日和應徵截止日，因此答案為 (B)。

5

何時是應徵截止日？

(A) **6 月 1 日**
(B) 6 月 20 日
(C) 7 月 15 日
(D) 7 月 20 日

解析

女子提到所有職位應徵的截止日都是 6 月 1 日（all applications are due by June 1），因此答案為 (A)。

6

請看圖表。男子感興趣的職位在哪個部門？

(A) **網路管理**
(B) 資訊發展
(C) 研發
(D) 業務

解析

男子提到他對網頁設計師的職缺有興趣（I'm interested in applying for a position as a web page designer），而表格裡網頁設計師所屬的部門為網路管理部門（Online Management），因此答案選 (A)。

04 旅遊／出差 p.101

STEP 1 題型演練

1 (B)   2 (A)

1

活動何時開始？

(A) 11 日
(B) 12 日
(C) 13 日

解析

女子在對話中段提到活動於 12 日開始（the event starts on the 12^(th)），因此答案為 (B)。

2

男子說「放心交給我吧」，意思為何？

(A) 他會去訂票。
(B) 他願意付機票錢。
(C) 他可以陪女子去。

解析

男子說出「you can count on me」，為針對女子請他預訂機票（you should book four tickets for the 11^(th)）的答覆，因此答案選 (A)。

STEP 2 常考用法

1 without a form of identification
2 put your carry-on baggage / in the overhead compartment
3 an aisle seat / a window seat
4 fill out this from
5 book two hotel rooms
6 The accommodations / fully booked

STEP 3 聽寫練習

1 (C)　　　　2 (B)

1

W Excuse me, but I think you <u>are in my seat</u>. My ticket says I'm in 5A, <u>the window seat</u>.

M Oh, really? Let me check my ticket. Hmm . . . Oh, I'm so sorry. It says that I'm <u>seated right behind you</u>. That was my mistake.

W That's no problem. I <u>don't mind changing seats</u> with you. <u>It will be easier</u> than having you move.

M That's so kind of you. Thank you so much. I'll <u>let the flight attendant know</u>.

女 不好意思，我想您坐到我的位子了。我機票上的座位是 5A 靠窗。

男 噢，真的嗎？我看一下我的票。嗯……噢，真的很抱歉。票上寫我的座位在您的正後方，我坐錯位子了。

女 沒關係，我不介意和您換座位，這樣會比您移動更容易。

男 非常謝謝您的好意，我會再跟空服員知會一聲。

前面					
4A	4B			4C	4D
5A	5B	走道		5C	5D
6A	6B			6C	6D
後面					

請看圖表。女子將會坐在哪裡？

(A) 5A
(B) 5B
(C) 6A
(D) 6B

解析

女子的座位為 5A，而男子的座位為 6A，但是女子表示願意去坐男子的座位（I don't mind changing seats with you），因此答案為 (C)。

2

W Hello. <u>I'm calling to sign up for</u> the Las Vegas Technology Exhibition <u>taking place next month</u>. My company would like to <u>register for a booth</u>.

M Okay. Is this your first time <u>attending the conference</u>?

W No, we have had a booth every year for the last 3 years.

M Oh, then registration should be very simple. What name <u>did you register under</u> last year? I can <u>use last year's records</u> to create a new registration for this year.

女 您好，我打這通電話是想報名參加下個月在拉斯維加斯舉行的科技展，我們公司想申請一個攤位。

男 好的。請問你們是第一次參展嗎？

女 不，我們這三年來每年都有一個攤位。

男 噢，那這樣申請就很簡單了。請問你們去年是用誰的名義登記的呢？我能用您去年的紀錄來登記今年的活動。

男子要求什麼資訊？
(A) 電子郵件地址
(B) 姓名
(C) 出貨單號
(D) 會議個人編號

解析

為了協助女子報名，男子向她詢問去年報名時所用的名字（What name did you register under last year?），因此答案為 (B)。

實戰演練 p.104

1 (B)	2 (A)	3 (D)
4 (C)	5 (D)	6 (A)

[1-3]

M Good afternoon. May I have your ID, please?
W Here you are.
M What is your final destination today? And will you be checking any bags?
W I'm going to Philadelphia, and, yes, I would like to check this bag, please.
M Okay. I see you are transferring in Tulsa. You have to get a new boarding pass when you get there, so please go to the airline counter as soon as you arrive.
W I see. Do I need to collect my baggage in Tulsa as well?
M No, your bag will go all the way to your final destination. You can pick it up at the baggage claim area there.

男 午安。方便看一下您的身分證嗎？
女 請。
男 請問您今天的目的地是哪裡？另外，您需要託運行李嗎？
女 我要去費城，然後對，我想託運這個包包。
男 好的。我看您將在塔爾薩轉機，您到那裡後必須拿一張新的登機證，所以請在抵達那裡之後，盡早前往機場櫃檯。
女 了解了。我需要在塔爾薩拿我的託運行李嗎？
男 不用，您的行李將直接掛到您的目的地，您到目的地的行李領取處提領就可以了。

字彙 **final destination** 目的地　**transfer** 轉乘
boarding pass 登機證　**collect** 提領（行李）
pick up 提領（行李）
baggage claim 行李領取處

1
男子要求什麼東西？
(A) 票
(B) 身分證件
(C) 登機證
(D) 預約編號

解析

男子要求女子出示身分證（May I have your ID, please?），因此答案為 (B)。

2
女子在塔爾薩應做什麼？
(A) 拿新的登機證
(B) 提領行李
(C) 要求換座位
(D) 出示護照

解析

男子請女子抵達塔爾薩後，要領取新的登機證（You have to get a new boarding pass when you get there），因此答案選 (A)。

3
女子會在哪裡拿到她託運的包包？
(A) 塔爾薩的出境登機門
(B) 費城的機場櫃檯
(C) 塔爾薩的行李領取處
(D) 費城的行李領取處

解析

女子詢問是否需要在塔爾薩領取行李，而後男子表示行李會送達最終目的地，因此請她抵達費城後再領取即可（your bag will go all the way to your final destination. You can pick it up at the baggage claim area there），因此答案為 (D)。

[4-6]

W1 What time do we have to check out tomorrow? Will we have time to come back to the hotel after our meeting with the partners at the Lakeview Law Firm?

M We should check out at 12 P.M., so I think we should bring our bags with us. I'm sure there is a place we can keep them at their office.

W2 Well, why don't we just ask the hotel if we can check out at a later time? It would be such a pain to bring our things all the way to the office.

W1 Good idea, Lisa. I don't mind paying a late checkout fee. It would be better to leave our bags at the hotel during the meeting.

M Hmm . . . let's check with the front desk. I think we can pay the fee by using the company card.

女1 我們明天什麼時候得退房？我們和湖景法律事務所的工作夥伴開完會後，還有時間回飯店嗎？

男 我們得在中午 12 點退房，所以我想我們應該把行李帶著。我確定他們的辦公室有地方可以讓我們放行李。

女2 嗯，不如我們問問看飯店能不能讓我們晚點退房？把行李拖到辦公室實在很不方便。

女1 好主意耶，麗莎。我不介意付延遲退房的費用，開會時還是把行李留在飯店比較好。

男 嗯……那我們跟櫃檯確認一下。我想我們可以用公司卡付帳。

字彙 check out（飯店）退房　fee 費用

4

談話的人彼此最有可能的關係為何？
(A) 家人
(B) 飯店員工
(C) 同事
(D) 朋友

解析

說話者要一同參加某個會議，表示彼此間的關係為同事較為合理，因此答案為 (C)。

5

談話的人明天要做什麼？
(A) 應徵工作
(B) 提前退房
(C) 搭計程車
(D) 參加會議

解析

女子提及明天的行程，並詢問會議結束後是否來得及回飯店（Will we have time to come back to the hotel after our meeting with the partners at the Lakeview Law Firm?），因此答案選 (D)。

6

男子接下來會做什麼？
(A) 和飯店櫃檯人員交談
(B) 退房
(C) 聯絡法律事務所討論會議事項
(D) 要求他的早餐早一點上

解析

男子提到會向飯店櫃檯確認（let's check with the front desk），表示他會詢問飯店櫃檯人員，因此答案為 (A)。

多益實戰單字 PART 3 UNIT ❶ - ❹　　p.106

A

1 (A)　　**2** (A)　　**3** (A)　　**4** (A)　　**5** (B)

B

1 get a hold of　**2** a final number
3 the application　**4** the details
5 under

C

1 hire more sales clerks
2 go over today's agenda
3 is fully booked on the day of
4 send them to you right away
5 approve your time off

05 設施／辦公室用品　　p.107

STEP 1 題型演練

1 (B)　　　**2** (C)

1

女子說「是時候升級一下影印機了」，意思為何？
(A) 辦公室需要整修。
(B) 需要新的影印機。
(C) 影印機需要修理。

男子提到這個月影印機已經故障三次了（The copy machine has broken down three times this month），由此可知女子這句話指的是需要一台新的影印機。

2

女子說她會做什麼？
(A) 寄電子郵件
(B) 購買新的影印機
(C) 詢問預算

解析

女子表示要向經理詢問是否有足夠的預算購買新的影印機（I'll ask the manager if we have enough money in the budget for a new one），因此答案為 (C)。

STEP 2 常考用法

1 office supply
2 put an order in for
3 use express delivery / urgent
4 call a repairman
5 parking structure / renovation / public parking area
6 on any of the premises

STEP 3 聽寫練習

| 1 (D) | 2 (A) |

1

> M　Do we have any more document envelopes? I need to send the new proposal to our team in Montreal, and I don't want to bend the documents.
> W1　Hmm . . . it seems that we have run out. I'll put an order in for some more. If it's urgent, you can buy some at the office supply store down the road, and the company will pay you back.
> W2　Actually, I picked some up on my way to work this morning. They are in the small supply closet on the first floor.
> M　Oh, that's great! You're a lifesaver, Beatrix.

男　我們還有公文封嗎？我得把新計畫書寄給我們蒙特婁的團隊，但我不想讓文件折到。
女1　嗯……我們好像用完了，我會再訂一些來。你如果急著用，可以到路上的辦公用品店買一些，公司會再把錢報給你。
女2　其實我今天早上上班時順路買了幾個，放在一樓的小置物櫃裡。
男　噢，太好了！碧翠絲你真是救星。

碧翠絲稍早做了什麼？
(A) 提早上班。
(B) 印了些文件。
(C) 清理置物櫃。
(D) 買了幾個信封。

解析

Beatrix（碧翠絲）表示今天早上來上班的路上買了一些信封（I picked some up (document envelopes) on my way to work this morning），因此答案為 (D)。

2

> M　Excuse me, ma'am, but I'm afraid you can't park here. We are going to do some construction here this afternoon.
> W　Construction? That isn't supposed to start until tomorrow.
> M　We just decided to start today because of the weather. You'll have to move your car to the south lot, unfortunately.
> W　Okay, well, thank you for the information. Do you know when the construction is expected to end?
> M　I'm not sure, but I don't expect it will take too long.

男　抱歉，女士，您恐怕不能把車停在這裡，我們今天下午會在這裡施工。
女　施工？那不是應該明天才開始的嗎？
男　因為天氣的關係，我們剛剛才決定今天動工。真的很抱歉，您得把車移到南邊的停車場才行。
女　嗯，好，感謝你告訴我。你知道施工預計什麼時候結束嗎？
男　我不確定，但我預計不會花太久時間。

根據男子的說法，最近有何決定？
(A) 提早開始施工
(B) 關閉南邊停車場
(C) 簽署新合約
(D) 改停車場名稱

解析

女子表示她以為停車場明天才開始施工（That isn't supposed to start until tomorrow），男子回她已經決定今天施工（We just decided to start today）。這表示最近才決定提前施工一事，因此答案為 (A)。

實戰演練

1 (C)	2 (B)	3 (D)
4 (C)	5 (A)	6 (B)

[1-3]

W Dan, I need a room with a projector for tomorrow's meeting. Are any of the conference rooms available?

M Hmm . . . it looks like all the rooms are booked. You could check out one of the portable projectors and set it up in a different room.

W That sounds kind of difficult. I've never used one of those projectors before, and I'm afraid that it might not work properly.

M Don't worry. You can ask someone from the IT Department to help. They can set up the projector for you. Just call them and request a specific time.

W Wow, that is exactly what I needed! Thank you so much.

女 丹，明天開會我需要一間有投影機的會議室。還有空的會議室嗎？

男 嗯……好像全部的會議室都被預約了。你可以借一台攜帶式投影機來裝在會議室。

女 聽起來有點難耶，我從來沒用過那種投影機，我怕它可能沒辦法正常運作。

男 別擔心，你可以找資訊科技部的同仁協助，他們可以幫你安裝投影機，只要打電話過去跟他們敲個明確的時間就行了。

女 哇，這正是我需要的。萬分感謝。

字彙 set up 安裝　work 運作　properly 正確地　specific 明確的

1

談話的主旨為何？
(A) 新進員工
(B) 轉調部門
(C) 會議所需設備
(D) 升級部分設施

解析

對話中提到「a room with a projector」（有投影機的會議室）、「portable projector」（攜帶式投影機）等內容，對話主題圍繞會議所需的設備，因此答案為 (C)。

2

根據男子的說法，女子可以怎麼做？
(A) 預約會議室開會
(B) 請資訊科技人員準備某項設備
(C) 明天休假
(D) 讓別人去開會

解析

男子表示女子可以向資訊科技部尋求協助，要求他們幫忙安裝投影機（You can ask someone from the IT Department to help. They can set up the projector for you），因此答案為 (B)。

3

女子擔心什麼？
(A) 她上班會遲到。
(B) 她老闆可能會生她的氣。
(C) 她的會議明天可能會取消。
(D) 她不知道該如何使用某項科技設備。

解析

女子表示自己未曾使用過那種投影機，擔心投影機無法正常運作（I've never used one of those projectors before, and I'm afraid that it might not work properly），因此答案為 (D)。

[4-6]

M Tomorrow, the bathrooms on this floor are going to be closed for repairs. Could you put together some signs to explain that we will need to use the second-floor bathrooms for the day?

W Of course. How long will they be closed?

M The repairs should only take a day, so just explain that the inconvenience will only be for tomorrow.

W Got it. Should we send an email out as well to let everyone know?

M I already did that this morning, so all the employees should know about it. Let's just hang the signs to remind everyone.

3

05 設施／辦公室用品

男 明天這層樓的洗手間將關閉維修。你能設置幾個告示,告訴大家當天得使用二樓的洗手間嗎?

女 當然可以。會關閉多久?

男 維修只需要一天,所以就跟大家說只有明天會造成大家的不便。

女 了解。我們要不要也寄個電子郵件通知大家?

男 我今天早上已經發過了,所以員工應該都聽說了。我們就掛幾個告示提醒大家吧。

字彙 repair 維修　inconvenience 不便
remind 提醒

4

談話的人在談什麼?

(A) 本季銷售額
(B) 新促銷
(C) 臨時異動
(D) 職場責任

解析

男子表示明天該層樓的洗手間將暫時封閉進行維修,要求對方設置告示(Tomorrow, the bathrooms on this floor are going to be closed for repairs. Could you put together some signs . . .),選項中最貼近此內容的說明為 (C)。

5

男子請女子做什麼?

(A) 製作幾個告示
(B) 分發促銷傳單
(C) 聯絡維修人員
(D) 打電話

解析

男子請女子張貼改用二樓洗手間的提醒公告(Could you put together some signs to explain that we will need to use the second-floor bathrooms for the day?),因此答案應選 (A)。

6

男子稍早做了什麼事?

(A) 針對某事做了幾個告示牌
(B) 通知員工某項異動
(C) 架設網站反映某些資訊
(D) 向老闆詢問更多資訊

解析

女子詢問是否要傳送電子郵件告訴大家(Should we send an email out as well to let everyone know?),而後男子表示早上他已經傳過了(I already did that this morning),因此答案為 (B)。

06 產品/服務　　　　　　　　　p.112

STEP 1 題型演練

1 (C)　　　　2 (A)

1

女子在哪個行業工作?

(A) 製造業
(B) 銀行業
(C) 出版業

解析

對話開頭處,女子表示自己在雜誌社工作,因此答案為 (C)。

2

女子為什麼打電話?

(A) 詢問退訂事宜
(B) 詢問欠款事宜
(C) 詢問折扣事宜

解析

第一段對話中,女子表示「You recently canceled your subscription」,並詢問「I wonder if I can ask you a few questions about why you did that」,表示她打電話的目的為詢問男子取消訂閱的原因,因此答案為 (A)。

STEP 2 常考用法

1 bring the original receipt / get a refund
2 pick up the tuxedo
3 sorry for the inconvenience
4 provide laundry service
5 carry home appliances
6 charges 70 dollars

1 (B)　　　　2 (D)

1

M Hi. My name is Abel Martin, and I'm calling about a product that I had refunded at your store last month. The shop assistant told me that I would receive the refund on my credit card within two weeks, but it has been over a month.

W I'm sorry to hear that. Do you have the receipt number with you?

M Yes, it's 554001.

W Let me see. It looks like your refund request wasn't approved. I'll approve it now. You should receive the refund by the end of the week. I'm very sorry for the delay.

M It's no problem.

男 您好，我叫亞伯·馬丁。我打電話來，是想詢問有關我上個月在您店裡退貨的商品。店員說那筆錢兩週內會退款到我的信用卡裡，但現在已經過一個多月了。

女 我很抱歉。您有收據號碼嗎？

男 有的，是 554001。

女 我查一下。您的退款看起來還沒有被核准，我現在就馬上核准。您會在週末之前收到退款，很抱歉耽擱了。

男 沒事的。

男子為什麼打電話？
(A) 他想更換產品。
(B) 他的退款有狀況。
(C) 店家沒有寄產品給他。
(D) 有份文件遺失了。

解析

男子提到自己是為了上個月辦理退貨一事打電話過來，表示已經過了一個多月卻仍未收到退款，因此答案為 (B)。

2

M Hello. This is Jake from Howser Communications. I have another document that I would like to add to our print order. Is that possible?

W Of course. If you email me the document and let me know how many pages you need, I can take care of it. That is no problem. And please let me know if it is a color or black and white order.

M Okay, I'll send you all of the information right now. When do you think everything will be ready?

W If you send me the new document right now, I can probably have everything done by Thursday.

男 您好，我是豪瑟傳播的傑克。我想在我們的印刷訂單上新增一份文件，可以嗎？

女 當然沒問題。您可以用電子郵件把文件寄給我，並告訴我您需要幾頁，由我來處理，完全沒有問題。也請告訴我您需要彩色還是黑白列印。

男 好，我馬上把資料全寄給您。您覺得什麼時候可以全部弄好呢？

女 如果您現在把新文件寄給我，我應該能在週四前做好。

談話的人在談什麼？
(A) 維修產品
(B) 設計商標
(C) 取消購買
(D) 修改訂單

解析

男子打電話表示想追加項目至印刷訂單中（I have another document that I would like to add to our print order），因此答案為 (D)。

PART

3

產品／服務

實戰演練

1 (A)	2 (C)	3 (D)
4 (C)	5 (D)	6 (A)

[1-3]

M Hi. I'm <u>looking for a new phone plan</u>. Can you show me <u>what options are available</u> for plans that include data?

W Certainly. As you can see on this chart, we have <u>several data plans</u>. The cost <u>depends on how much data is provided</u>. Our 2-gigabyte plan is <u>the most popular one</u> right now.

M Hmm . . . well . . . I need at least 3 gigabytes per month, so I <u>don't think that would work for me</u>.

W Well, you can see here that we have one plan with more than 3 gigabytes. <u>How does that look to you</u>?

M That sounds perfect. Can I <u>sign up for this plan</u> today?

W Absolutely. <u>Let me get the paperwork</u> for you to <u>fill out</u>, and we can <u>set up your phone</u> right away.

男 您好，我在看新的通話方案。您能讓我看看現有選項中包含流量的方案嗎？

女 好的。就像您在這張表上看到的，我們有好幾個不同的流量方案，費用是根據提供的數據量來算的。我們目前最受歡迎的是 2GB 的方案。

男 嗯……但是我每個月至少需要 3GB，所以我想這不適合我。

女 好的，您可以看一下這裡，我們有一個流量超過 3GB 的方案。您覺得怎麼樣？

男 聽起來很棒。我今天就能申辦這個方案嗎？

女 當然可以。我拿資料給您填寫一下，然後我們就可以立刻開始設定您的電話。

字彙 option 選項　available（物）可得的
include 包括　several 數個
depend on 根據……　popular 受歡迎的
at least 至少　paperwork 資料
fill out 填寫（表格）　set up 設定

方案	流量	月租費
A	500MB	$15
B	1GB	$30
C	2GB	$45
D	5GB	$60

1

談話的人最有可能在哪裡？
(A) 通訊行
(B) 會計事務所
(C) 客服中心
(D) 資訊科技研討會

解析

文中提到 phone（電話）、plan（方案）、data（流量）等單字，且男子在詢問通話資費，表示談話者在通訊行內，因此答案為 (A)。

2

男子想做什麼？
(A) 升級他的流量服務
(B) 取消他現有的電話服務
(C) 申辦新的電話服務
(D) 應徵客服工作

解析

男子提到自己正在找新的通話方案（I'm looking for a new phone plan），因此答案應選 (C)。

3

請看圖表。男子將為新方案付多少月租費？
(A) 15 美元
(B) 30 美元
(C) 45 美元
(D) 60 美元

解析

女子提到有一個超過 3GB 的方案（you can see here that we have one plan with more than 3 gigabytes），而後男子表示要申請該方案。可知男子選擇的是表格中的 D 方案，費用為 60 美元，因此答案為 (D)。

[4-6]

W Hello. This is Adela from Davis Repairs. I am on my way to your office to repair your copy machine, but I think I'll be late because of the traffic jam.

M Oh, I'm sorry to hear that, but thank you for letting us know. What time should we expect you?

W Well, I was supposed to be there by 3 P.M., but I think I will arrive a little after 4 P.M. Is that all right?

M Yes, it's no problem. When you arrive, please come to the north entrance, and someone will let you in.

W All right. Thank you so much and sorry again for the inconvenience.

女 您好，我是戴維斯維修的艾德拉。我正在前往您辦公室修理影印機的路上，不過因為塞車的關係，我想我可能會遲到。

男 噢，真糟糕，謝謝您通知我們。那我們幾點能等到您來呢？

女 嗯，我本來應該在下午 3 點前到，但現在我想我會在下午 4 點多抵達。這樣可以嗎？

男 可以，沒問題。您到的時候請走北邊的入口，會有人讓您進來。

女 好，非常感謝您，再次為造成您的不便說聲抱歉。

字彙 repair 維修　traffic jam 塞車
be supposed to（被認為）應該……
entrance 入口　inconvenience 不便

4
女子為什麼打電話？
(A) 她迷路了。
(B) 她用影印機需要協助。
(C) 她會遲到。
(D) 她想取消會面。

解析

女子表示現在在前往對方辦公室的路上，但是因為塞車，應該會遲到（I think I'll be late because of the traffic jam），因此答案為 (C)。

5
女子提到什麼問題？
(A) 某項設備故障了。
(B) 她忘記有約。
(C) 她的車故障了。
(D) 路上塞車很嚴重。

解析

女子提及遲到的原因為塞車，因此答案應選 (D) The road traffic is heavy。

6
男子和女子說了什麼？
(A) 出入大樓的方法
(B) 影印機的位置
(C) 影印機的問題
(D) 他抵達的時間

解析

男子請女子從北邊的入口進來，那邊會有人讓她進入大樓，因此答案為 (A)。

07 購物／休假 　　　　　p.117

STEP 1 題型演練

　1 (A)　　　2 (B)

1
女子的問題為何？
(A) 她房間的狀況不好。
(B) 她房間太吵。
(C) 她房間空間不足。

解析

女子表示自己的房間內味道很可怕（It smells terrible），因此答案為 (A)。

2
男子最有可能是誰？
(A) 銷售人員
(B) 飯店員工
(C) 業務代表

解析

女子向男子訴說自己對房間的不滿（file a complaint about my room），由此可知男子應為飯店員工，因此答案為 (B)。

1 offering a 10% discount / make an online purchase
2 return an item / bring your original receipt
3 was overcharged for
4 speak with a manager
5 get an additional discount
6 itinerary / do some sightseeing

STEP 3 聽寫練習

1 (C)   2 (B)

1

> W Hello. Is your Memorial Day Sale still going on?
> M It certainly is. All of our spring clothing lines are up to 50% off, and we have a buy-one-get-one-free deal on any pair of jeans.
> W Oh, great. I have a coupon that I received in the mail. Can I use it on sale items as well?
> M Unfortunately, sale prices cannot be combined with any other coupons or promotions. I'm sorry about that, but you can save that coupon and use it after the sale ends.
> W Okay, well, I think I'll just take a look around for now. Thank you.

> 女 您好。你們的國殤紀念日特賣會還在進行嗎？
> 男 當然，我們全系列春裝商品最高可享五折，任何牛仔褲也都買一送一。
> 女 噢，太好了。我有從郵件裡拿到一張優惠券，特賣品也能使用嗎？
> 男 很遺憾，特價商品不能跟任何優惠券或促銷做搭配。我很抱歉，但您可以把那張優惠券留到特賣結束後再使用。
> 女 嗯，好，那我想我現在先逛一下就好。謝謝。

男子建議女子做什麼？
(A) 用優惠券買特賣品
(B) 買幾條牛仔褲
(C) 將優惠券留到之後再用
(D) 看看特價的新品

解析

男子建議女子先留著優惠券，等到特賣活動結束後再使用（you can save that coupon and use it after the sale ends），因此答案應選 (C)。

2

> M Hello. I'd like to return this item, please.
> W All right, sir, I can certainly help you with that. Do you have the credit card that you purchased the item with?
> M Oh, no, I don't have it with me right now, but I have the receipt. Can you just give me the refund in cash?
> W Unfortunately, we have a policy against that. You will have to return with the card before I can give you a refund on the product.
> M I see. Well, I'll have to come back another time then. Thank you anyway.

> 男 您好，我想退還這件商品。
> 女 好的，先生，由我來幫您處理。您有沒有攜帶購買這項商品時刷的信用卡呢？
> 男 噢，沒有，我現在沒帶在身邊，但我有收據。您能直接退現金給我嗎？
> 女 抱歉，這有違我們公司的規定。您必須把信用卡帶來，我才能給您這項商品的退款。
> 男 了解，那我改天再來。還是謝謝您。

發生了什麼狀況？
(A) 某商品賣完了。
(B) 男子沒帶信用卡。
(C) 產品毀損了。
(D) 女子沒帶任何現金。

解析

男子欲將商品退貨，但是沒帶信用卡，無法辦理退款，因此答案為 (B)。

實戰演練 p.120

1 (A)	2 (A)	3 (C)
4 (D)	5 (B)	6 (C)

[1-3]

M Hello. I'm calling because I stayed there last night, and I think I left my wallet in the room when I checked out.

W You did? Okay, let me see what I can do. What room were you staying in?

M Room 505. I was there for three nights and checked out this morning.

W Yes, it seems that a member of the staff gave your wallet to the lost and found here. You can come by and pick it up whenever it's convenient for you.

M Oh, no. I've already flown back home, so there is no way I can physically pick it up. Can you have it shipped to my home?

W You'll have to speak with a manager about that. Please hold on one moment.

男 您好。我打這通電話,是因為我昨晚住你們飯店,但好像在退房時把皮夾忘在房間裡了。

女 真的嗎?好,我想想該怎麼做。請問您住幾號房呢?

男 505 號房。我住了三個晚上,是今天早上退房的。

女 有的,我們的一名同仁似乎已經把您的皮夾送到我們的失物招領處了。您方便的話可以隨時過來領取。

男 噢,不,我已經坐飛機回國了,所以我無法親自去拿。您能寄到我家嗎?

女 這件事您得和我們經理談談。請稍待片刻。

字彙 wallet(尤指男用的)皮夾
physically 實際(到場) ship 運送

1

女子最有可能在哪裡工作?
(A) 飯店
(B) 機場
(C) 計程車公司
(D) 餐廳

解析

男子表示自己退房時把皮夾忘在房內沒有帶走(I think I left my wallet in the room when I checked out),而後女子問他之前住在哪一間房間(What room were you staying in?)。這段話顯示女子應在飯店工作較為合理,因此答案為 (A)。

2

男子提到什麼問題?
(A) 他掉了皮夾。
(B) 他想預約一個房間。
(C) 他想和經理談談。
(D) 他忘了預約編號。

解析

男子表示退房時把皮夾忘在房內未帶走(I think I left my wallet in the room when I checked out),因此答案為 (A)。

3

女子接下來最有可能做什麼?
(A) 寄皮夾給男子
(B) 關閉接待處
(C) 打電話給她的經理
(D) 為男子保留房間

解析

對話最後,女子請男子跟經理談(You'll have to speak with a manager about that),並請他稍待一會,因此答案應選 (C)。

[4-6]

W Good morning. How may I help you?

M1 Hi. Do you have whole wheat flour? I'd like to make a large purchase for my bakery.

W Whole wheat flour? I think we do, but let me check. Hey, Leeroy, do we carry whole wheat flour?

M2 Yeah, but not at this location. You have to go to our downtown store for that. Or we can order it and have it delivered here.

M1 Okay, in that case I'll just head to the other location. Thanks so much for the help.

女 早安。有什麼我能幫您的嗎?

男1 嗨。您有全麥麵粉嗎?我的麵包店想大量採購。

女 全麥麵粉嗎?我想是有的,但讓我確認一下。嘿,勒萊,我們店裡有全麥麵粉嗎?

男2 有,但不在這家店。您得去我們市中心的分店買,或是我們這裡訂購再讓麵粉送過來。

男1 好,這樣的話,我還是直接去那家店好了。感謝您的幫忙。

字彙 whole wheat flour 全麥麵粉
make a purchase 採購 deliver 運送

4

男子正想買什麼東西？

(A) 美術用品
(B) 烤箱
(C) 花
(D) 麵粉

解析

男子詢問是否有賣全麥麵粉（Do you have whole wheat flour?），因此答案為 (D)。

5

關於這項商品，勒萊說了什麼？

(A) 店裡賣完了。
(B) 別家分店有賣。
(C) 他今天早上賣出最後一份。
(D) 以折扣價格特賣中。

解析

女子詢問店內是否有全麥麵粉（do we carry whole wheat flour?），Leeroy（勒萊）回答我們這家店沒有（not at this location），因此答案應選 (B)。雖然對話中提到店內沒有全麥麵粉，但這是指這家分店沒有賣，並非全店賣光的意思，因此千萬不能誤選 (A) 作為答案。

6

顧客接下來最有可能做什麼？

(A) 訂購產品
(B) 討價還價
(C) 前往另一家分店
(D) 要求和經理談

解析

對話最後，男子表示會去別家分店（I'll just head to the other location），因此答案為 (C)。

08 交通／公共場所　　　　　p.122

STEP 1 題型演練

1 (C)　　　2 (C)

1

男子可能會搭哪種車去水牛城？

(A) 特快車
(B) 地下鐵
(C) 普通車

解析

男子表示要搭乘較快出發的火車（I'll take whichever is departing sooner），接著女子請他搭普通車（That would be the local train），因此答案為 (C)。

2

男子接下來會做什麼？

(A) 查看列車時刻表
(B) 買車票
(C) 前往月台

解析

女子告訴男子可以在 8 號月台搭乘列車（You can get the train at platform 8），因此答案為 (C)。

STEP 2 常考用法

1 have to get a medical checkup
2 a lot of pedestrians
3 got stuck in traffic
4 check out five books
5 to catch the 11 o'clock train
6 the most common symptoms

STEP 3 聽寫練習

1 (C)　　　2 (B)

1

M Excuse me. Can I use this ticket to transfer buses? I'm trying to get to Madrid.
W Let's see. I'm sorry, but bus tickets can only be used to transfer if your ticket is less than two hours old. You bought your ticket three hours ago, so you must buy a new ticket to get to your destination.
M Oh, I see. Do you know where the ticket office is?
W It's just right there next to the elevators.

男 不好意思，我可以用這張票轉乘公車嗎？我想到馬德里。
女 請讓我看看。很抱歉，公車票的轉乘時限是兩小時之內。您的票是三小時前購買的，所以您必須買新的票才能搭到您的目的地。
男 噢，我了解了。您知道售票處在哪嗎？
女 就在電梯旁邊。

男子接下來最有可能做什麼？
(A) 去火車站
(B) 搭電梯
(C) **買票到馬德里**
(D) 到站台等巴士

解析

男子得知須購買一張新的票才能前往馬德里，便詢問女子售票處的位置（Oh, I see. Do you know where the ticket office is?），因此答案為 (C)。

2

M Hello. My name is Keith Little. I <u>have an appointment</u> for an X-ray at 2:30 P.M. today.

W All right, I see <u>this is your first time</u> to visit our office. Here, please <u>fill out these documents</u> while you wait. A nurse will call you when <u>the doctor is ready to see you</u>.

M Great. Do you need <u>a copy of my insurance card</u>? I have it right here.

W Oh, yes, thank you. I'll <u>make a copy of it</u>.

男 您好，我叫基斯·利特。我今天下午2點30分預約了X光檢查。

女 好的。這是您第一次來我們診所，候診時請填寫這些文件。等醫師準備好時會有護士叫您。

男 太好了。您需要我的健保卡影本嗎？我有，在這裡。

女 噢，要的，謝謝。我影印一下。

時間	醫師
12:30-1:30	凱利醫師
2:00-3:00	李醫師
3:30-4:30	帕默醫師
5:00-6:00	楊醫師

請看圖表。男子將和誰見面照X光？
(A) 凱利醫師
(B) **李醫師**
(D) 帕默醫師
(C) 楊醫師

解析

男子表示約診時間為2點30分（I have an appointment for an X-ray at 2:30 P.M. today）。看完表格後會發現，該時間介於2點至3點間，而該時段看診的醫師為 Dr. Lee（李醫師），因此答案為 (B)。

實戰演練 p.125

p.125

1 (D)	**2** (A)	**3** (B)
4 (B)	**5** (A)	**6** (B)

[1-3]

W Hello. I'd like to <u>return</u> these books, please. Here is <u>my library card</u>.

M All right, let's take a look. Oh, it seems that <u>one of these books is overdue</u> by a week. You'll have to <u>pay a $2.00 late fee</u>.

W Oh, really? I didn't realize that it was late. Hmm . . . <u>I don't have any cash</u> on me. Is it possible to <u>pay by card</u>?

M I'm afraid not. But there is <u>an ATM in the lobby</u> that you can use. I <u>suggest taking care of it</u> today to <u>avoid paying any additional charges</u>.

女 您好，我要還這些書。這是我的借書證。

男 好的，我看一下。噢，其中一本書好像已經逾期一週了，您得付2美元的逾期罰款。

女 噢，真的嗎？我沒注意到逾期了。嗯……我身上沒帶現金。我能刷卡嗎？

男 恐怕不行，不過您可以使用大廳那裡的提款機。為了避免罰款增加，我建議您今天就處理這件事。

字彙 return 歸還　overdue 逾期的
late fee 逾期罰款
ATM (= Automated Teller Machine) 自動提款機
additional 額外的　charge 費用

1
談話的人最有可能在哪裡？
(A) 電影院
(B) 大賣場
(C) 書店
(D) **圖書館**

解析

聽到還書（return these books）、逾期罰款（late fee）等單字，表示談話的人在圖書館。

2
男子建議女子做什麼？
(A) **今天就繳交罰款**
(B) 買一本書
(C) 別的時間再來
(D) 多借幾本書

片名	時間	價錢
《終戰》	上午10點	6美元
	上午11點	7美元
	下午3點	8美元
	晚間7點	9美元

解析

對話最後，男子建議女子最好今天處理完畢，以免要付更多的錢（I suggest taking care of it today to avoid paying any additional charges），表示要求她今天就繳交逾期罰款，因此答案為 (A)。

3

男子說「恐怕不行」，最有可能的意思為何？

(A) 他將取消罰款。

(B) 女子不能刷卡。

(C) 逾期罰款很重。

(D) 附近沒有提款機。

解析

女子詢問是否可用信用卡付款（Is it possible to pay by card?），而題目中引用的話「I'm afraid not」為對此提問的答覆。這表示不能用信用卡付款，因此答案為 (B)。

[4-6]

M Hello, Rachel. I'm thinking of seeing a movie tomorrow. Do you want to go with me?

W Sure, that sounds fun. What do you have in mind?

M Well, I want to see the new action film *The Last Battle*, but I'm not sure what time would be good. What do you think?

W Hmm . . . Let's see a morning show because it's cheaper. How about the earliest one?

M Good idea. We could have lunch after the show, too. I know a good restaurant near the theater.

男 喂，瑞秋，我明天想看電影，你想不想跟我一起去？

女 當然好啊，聽起來不賴。你想看哪一部？

男 嗯，我想看最新的動作片《終戰》，但我不確定哪個時間比較好。你覺得呢？

女 嗯……早場比較便宜，就早上看吧。看最早的一場怎麼樣？

男 好主意，我們看完電影還可以去吃午餐。我知道電影院附近有一家不錯的餐廳。

字彙 have something in mind 有想法

4

男子為什麼打電話？

(A) 為了問路

(B) 為了邀女子出門

(C) 為了取消預約

(D) 為了詢問一筆花費

解析

對話開頭處，男子約女子一起去看電影（I'm thinking of seeing a movie tomorrow），(B) 意即向女子提出邀約，故為正確答案。

5

請看圖表。談話的人買一張票得付多少錢？

(A) 6 美元

(B) 7 美元

(C) 8 美元

(D) 9 美元

解析

談話者兩人決定要看最早的場次，電影最早開演的時間為上午 10 點，而該場次的票價為 6 美元，因此答案為 (A)。

6

關於餐廳，男子怎麼說？

(A) 剛開不久。

(B) 靠近電影院。

(C) 正在整修。

(D) 風評不佳。

解析

對話最後，男子提到電影院附近的餐廳（I know a good restaurant near the theater）。(B) 將 near 改寫為 close，故為正確答案。

多益實戰單字 PART 3 UNIT **05** - **08**　　　p.127

A

1 (A)　　2 (A)　　3 (A)　　4 (A)　　5 (B)

B

1 carry   **2** inconvenience

3 urgent   **4** set up

5 itinerary

C

1 got stuck in traffic

2 are up to 50% off

3 isn't supposed to start until

4 get a medical checkup on a regular basis

5 fill out this form / fill this form out

PART 4 | 簡短獨白 Short Talks

01 廣告

STEP 1 題型演練

1 (A)   2 (C)

1

廣告內容為何？

(A) 賣二手書的機會

(B) 買二手書的機會

(C) 一家大學書店

解析

說話者提到 Barney's Books（巴尼書屋）將提供最優惠的價格給想賣書的學生（Here at Barney's Books, we offer the best prices to students selling their books），因此答案為 (A)。

2

男子為什麼說：「我們保證給你同樣的價格」？

(A) 表示書店提供最好的書

(B) 解釋價格這麼高的原因

(C) 表示商店提供最優惠的價格

解析

獨白中提到：「如果大學書店價格更好，我們保證給你同樣的價格」（if the university bookstore offers a better price, we guarantee that we will match its price），因此答案為 (C)。

STEP 2 常考用法

1 celebrate our grand opening

2 stop by / find out more about this deal

3 only last until

4 conveniently located in the heart of

5 enter a contest / write down your name

6 convention center / spacious meeting rooms / accommodate

STEP 3 聽寫練習

1 (C)   2 (A)

1

M Nothing is worse than slow download speeds. That's why Next Edge Internet works hard to bring the fastest Internet speeds possible to our city. We offer a wide range of high-speed Internet packages that will fit the needs of every customer. Check out our website for details on our home and business Internet plans. Next Edge: it doesn't get any faster.

男 沒有什麼比下載速度緩慢更糟糕的了。就是因為這樣，新嶄網路才會致力提供堪稱我們城市最快的網速。我們提供多種高速上網方案，能滿足每一位顧客的需求。家庭和企業網路方案的詳細內容，請上我們官網查詢。新嶄網路，誰與爭鋒。

廣告提到的服務為何？

(A) 手機服務

(B) 廣告服務

(C) 網路供應商服務

(D) 電腦維修服務

解析

獨白中提到 Next Edge Internet（新嶄網路）努力提供該地區最為快速的網路（Next Edge Internet works hard to bring the fastest Internet speeds possible to our city），因此答案為 (C)。

2

W Do you spend hours and hours studying a foreign language but aren't satisfied with the results? Well, then Word Wise is just the app for you! We understand how difficult it can be to learn a new language, so that's why we have developed an easy way to learn new vocabulary every day right on your mobile phone anytime and anywhere! It is the simplest and most convenient way to improve your vocabulary. Signing up is fast and easy, so download Word Wise today!

女 你是不是花了大把時間學外語,結果還是不甚滿意呢?若是這樣,「字智」這一套應用程式就是專門為你所設計的。我們了解學習新語言有多麼困難,所以為你創造了一個簡單的方法,只要一機在手,隨時隨地都能學習新單字。提高單字量就靠這招,超簡單、超方便。註冊也很快很輕鬆,現在就下載「字智」吧!

說話者強調此應用程式的什麼特點?
(A) 簡單好用。
(B) 不貴。
(C) 客服很棒。
(D) 非常時尚。

解析

說話者表示,這款應用程式是提升單字量最簡單、最方便的方法(It is the simplest and most convenient way to improve your vocabulary),因此答案為 (A)。

實戰演練

p.133

1 (C)	2 (D)	3 (D)
4 (D)	5 (C)	6 (A)

[1-3]

M Are you looking for a way to lose weight this year? Here at Flying Jay Fitness, we can help! Our gyms have the most modern equipment available for every kind of exercise routine. For new gym members, we also provide one month of free personal training to help you get started. And for a limited time, we are offering a 20% discount on yearly memberships! Start the new year right with Flying Jay Fitness!

男 今年想要減重嗎?來飛行傑伊健身,我們助你一臂之力!我們健身房有最新型的健身器材,適合各種日常鍛鍊。針對新會員,我們還提供一個月的免費私人教練課程幫你起步。我們也限時提供年費會員八折優惠。新的一年,就從飛行傑伊健身開始吧!

字彙 lose weight 減重　　equipment 器材
routine 日常的

1

打廣告的企業為何?
(A) 醫療診所
(B) 修車廠
(C) 健身房
(D) 高爾夫球場

解析

獨白中提到若要尋找減重的方法,Flying Jay Fitness(飛行傑伊健身)可以提供協助(Are you looking for a way to lose weight this year? Here at Flying Jay Fitness, we can help!),表示該篇獨白為健身房的廣告,因此答案為 (C)。

2

顧客能免費得到什麼?
(A) 會員資格
(B) 專車接送
(C) 運動器材
(D) 私人教練課程

解析

獨白中提到新會員可以享有一個月的免費私人教練課程(For new gym members, we also provide one month of free personal training to help you get started),因此答案應選 (D)。

3

客戶以哪種會員身分可享特別折扣?
(A) 1 個月
(B) 3 個月
(C) 6 個月
(D) 12 個月

解析

一年會員可享有會費八折的優惠(we are offering a 20% discount on yearly memberships),因此答案為 (D)。

[4-6]

W In order to celebrate the grand opening of the Manoa location, Percy's Department Store is having its biggest sale of the year! You can get up to 30% off products, including fashion, cosmetics, and outdoor gear, at all of our stores. What is even better is that we are offering coupons for an additional 10% discount only at the newly opened store. Other stores, such as those in Pikoi and Windward, offer only 30% discounts. This sale only lasts until Monday. And don't forget to visit our website to find coupons that will help you save even more!

女 為歡慶馬諾阿分店盛大開幕，波西百貨今年最大檔特賣正在進行中！我們所有店鋪的時尚單品、化妝品、戶外休閒用具等多項商品，最高可達七折優惠。更好康的是，我們還提供額外再打九折的優惠券，最新分店獨家限定；皮科伊及溫沃德等其他分店只提供七折優惠。優惠只到週一。別忘了上我們官網下載優惠券，它會幫您省更多！

字彙 cosmetics 化妝品　gear 用具
additional 額外的

```
波西百貨優惠券
到期日：6月15日
─────────────────
額外再打九折
─────────────────
每人限用一張優惠券
可搭配任何實體促銷
```

4

廣告內容為何？
(A) 新服務
(B) 新產品
(C) 店家搬遷
(D) 特賣

解析

獨白中提到 Percy's Department Store（波西百貨）正在舉辦最大檔的特賣活動（Percy's Department Store is having its biggest sale of the year!），因此答案為 (D)。

5

說話者說週一會發生什麼事？
(A) 新分店將開幕。
(B) 某項產品將上市。
(C) 特賣活動將結束。
(D) 某活動將開始。

解析

獨白中提到特惠活動僅到週一截止（This sale only lasts until Monday），表示特惠活動將於週一結束，因此答案為 (C)。

6

請看圖表。在哪家分店可使用這張優惠券？
(A) 馬諾阿
(B) 皮科伊
(C) 溫沃德
(D) 所有的派西百貨分店

解析

獨白中提到額外提供的九折優惠券，僅限新開幕的分店使用（we are offering coupons for an additional 10% discount only at the newly opened store），因此答案為 (A)。

PART 4

02 廣播
p.135

STEP 1 題型演練

1 (C)　　2 (C)

1

聽眾被建議做什麼？
(A) 待在室內
(B) 使用大眾運輸
(C) 走替代道路

解析

根據廣播的內容，14 號公路預計封閉至 9 月底（Highway 14 between Denver and Culver City will be closed until the end of September），說話者建議這段時間改走 36 號公路（Drivers should use Highway 36 to travel between the two cities during this time），因此答案選 (C)。

2

聽眾接下來會聽到什麼？
(A) 訪談
(B) 商業新聞
(C) 國際新聞

解析

獨白最後提到接下來要播報的是國際新聞，請聽眾不要轉台（Stay tuned for international news coming up next），因此答案為 (C)。

STEP 2 常考用法

1 after this commercial break / stay tuned
2 use public transportation / the expansion of the lanes
3 will be interviewing the mayor / construction project
4 continue to be extremely hot / humid
5 Commuters / will be closed in August
6 is expected to drop dramatically

STEP 3 聽寫練習

1 (A)　　　　2 (C)

1

> **M** Good morning and welcome back to KKL Radio. Today, we have a special guest, Dr. Alicia Gonzalez, a professor of economics and finance at the University of Colorado. For the next hour, Dr. Gonzalez is going to help us understand how the financial crisis is affecting small businesses in the area. She will also share some advice on how you can handle the crisis better. At the end of the show, we will take some time for Dr. Gonzalez to answer your questions, so I invite you listeners to call in at that time.

> 男 早安，歡迎回到 KKL 電台。今天我們有位特別來賓：來自科羅拉多大學的經濟及財金教授，艾莉西亞‧岡薩雷斯博士。接下來的一個小時，岡薩雷斯博士將協助我們了解金融危機對地方小型企業的影響，也會給我們一些有關危機處理的建議。在節目的最後，我們也會保留一些時間讓岡薩雷斯博士回答問題，歡迎各位聽眾到時踴躍來電。

節目鼓勵聽眾做什麼？
(A) 來電問問題
(B) 創立小型企業
(C) 參加公開會議
(D) 試著省更多錢

解析

說話者在最後一段邀請聽眾打電話進來（I invite you listeners to call in at that time），因此答案應為 (A)。

2

> **W** Thanks for listening to Radio MBB. Don't forget that the Douglas County Fair will be in town until this Sunday, October 21. You can enjoy the fair rides, the games, and, of course, the fair food! On Saturday, there will be a giant pumpkin competition. You can find out who grew the biggest pumpkin. It will be great fun for all the family, and you can get free pumpkin seeds. On Sunday, the fair will feature a special musical artist, the Jason Byer Band! Tickets are going fast, so check out the county fair website before it's too late.

> 女 感謝您收聽 MBB 電台。別忘了道格拉斯縣市集舉行到這週日 10 月 21 日。您可以玩遊樂設施、遊戲，當然也有市集美食！週六會有巨型南瓜大賽，您將會知道種出最大南瓜的高手是誰。此外，還有免費南瓜種子可以領，闔家都歡樂。週日還有特別的音樂表演團體——傑森拜爾樂團的演出！門票不等人，趕快上縣辦市集官網查詢，以免向隅。

說話者說「門票不等人」，意思為何？
(A) 門票特價出售。
(B) 看表演不需門票。
(C) 表演很受歡迎。
(D) 歌手大受好評。

解析

廣播先提到樂團的表演後，接著表示門票很快會銷售一空。這段話可以理解為建議聽眾盡快購票的意思，因此答案選 (C) A show is very popular。

實戰演練　　　　　　　　　　　　　　p.138

1 (D)	2 (B)	3 (C)
4 (A)	5 (B)	6 (C)

[1-3]

M Thanks for joining us on WTZ Radio for the local sports news. Tomorrow is finally the big game between our own Wildcats and their rival, the Bears. This is the last game of the season, so there will be several special events happening at the game. The first 100 people to arrive at the baseball stadium will receive a free Wildcats baseball cap, so you should get there early. In addition, if the Wildcats hit a homerun, Tony's Tacos will give away one free taco per customer after the game! If you can't make it to see the game live, you can always catch the game on the local TV channel.

男 感謝您一起收聽 WTZ 電台的地方體育新聞。明天我們的地主野貓隊和它的勁敵熊熊隊的大對決終於要登場啦。這是本賽季最後一場賽事，比賽期間有一些特別的活動。前 100 名到棒球場的觀眾將獲得免費的野貓隊棒球帽，想要就得趁早來。此外，如果野貓隊轟出一支全壘打，湯尼塔可屋將在比賽後免費贈送每位客人一份塔可餅。如果您沒辦法準時收看直播，之後還可以在地方電視頻道上觀看重播。

字彙 local 地方的　rival 對手
in addition 此外　give away 贈送、分發
make it 及時趕上

1
報導的主旨為何？
(A) 賽事取消
(B) 球隊有新血加入
(C) 新體育場開幕
(D) 將有一場重要比賽

解析
獨白中提到有兩個隊伍將進行一場重要的比賽，以及介紹相關的活動，因此答案應選 (D) An important game taking place。

2
說話者為什麼說「想要就得趁早來」？
(A) 天氣會不太好。
(B) 免費贈品數量有限。
(C) 停車空間有限。
(D) 門票快賣完了。

解析
獨白中提到前 100 名入場者將獲贈帽子（The first 100 people to arrive at the baseball stadium will receive a free Wildcats baseball cap），表示免費贈品的數量有限，因此答案為 (B)。

3
根據報導，球隊如果擊出一支全壘打，將會發生什麼事？
(A) 球隊將贏得獎杯。
(B) 觀眾可以收藏球。
(C) 一家餐廳將贈送免費食物。
(D) 比賽將結束。

解析
獨白中提到若擊出全壘打，比賽後餐廳將免費贈送塔可餅（if the Wildcats hit a homerun, Tony's Tacos will give away one free taco per customer after the game），因此答案選 (C) 贈送免費食物。

[4-6]

W And now for your local weather. Overall, temperatures will be warm, but it looks like we will be getting more rain this week. It is not a surprise during hurricane season here in Louisiana. But don't get too depressed. Fortunately, it is going to be sunny this coming Friday, so I suggest you take this chance to enjoy some time outdoors. It would be a great time to check out the newly constructed park on 5th Avenue.

女 現在來關心一下本地天氣。氣溫方面，整體來說會相當溫暖，不過這週的降雨可能還會增加。畢竟現在是路易斯安那州的颶風季，所以這並不令人意外。然而也不需要太沮喪。很棒的是這週五太陽會露臉，我建議大家趁機到戶外走走、享受一下。這也是參觀第五大道剛落成的新公園的絕佳時機。

字彙 temperature 氣溫　depressed 沮喪的
outdoors 在戶外　constructed 蓋好的

4
說話者表示這週將發生什麼事？
(A) 會繼續下雨。
(B) 某活動將因為天氣而取消。
(C) 將有暴風雪。
(D) 一棟建築將蓋好。

解析

獨白中提到預計本週會降下更多的雨（it looks like we will be getting more rain this week），因此答案為 (A)。

5

說話者說「畢竟現在是颶風季，所以這並不令人意外」，意思為何？
(A) 颶風無人能預測。
(B) 這是這段期間的典型天氣。
(C) 雨將停止。
(D) 風會很大。

解析

先提到預計會降下更多的雨，而後接著說道：「畢竟現在是颶風季，所以這並不令人意外」，因此答案應選 (B)。

6

說話者建議何時外出？
(A) 週二
(B) 週三
(C) 週五
(D) 週日

解析

獨白中提到本週五將會放晴，建議大家享受戶外的時光（it is going to be sunny this coming Friday, so I suggest you take this chance to enjoy some time outdoors），因此答案為 (C)。

03 電話留言

p.140

STEP 1 題型演練

1 (A)　　　　2 (B)

1

男子想給聽者什麼消息？
(A) 有人想買他的房子。
(B) 有人想賣房子給他。
(C) 有一對夫婦想親自見他。

解析

獨白開頭提到他帶一對夫婦看了聽者想賣掉的房子，而他們看過後決定出價購買（I showed a couple your house for sale, and they made an offer to buy it!），因此答案為 (A)。

2

說話者請聽者做什麼？
(A) 出個價
(B) 聯絡他
(C) 離開鎮上

解析

獨白最後請對方告知何時有空（Let me know when you are available），因此答案為 (B)。

STEP 2 常考用法

1 I am calling about
2 I have an inquiry about
3 I will be out of town
4 You can reach me at
5 Feel free to contact me
6 am responding to the request

STEP 3 聽寫練習

1 (D)　　　　2 (A)

1

W Hello. I'm calling from Lakeshore Telecommunications about your monthly phone bill. It seems that you still haven't paid last month's bill, so we have to charge you a late fee. Unfortunately, because your payment is more than 10 days late, the charge will be 10% of your total bill. Please pay your bill plus the late fee as soon as possible. As always, you can submit payments by phone, by mail, or online. If you have any questions, don't hesitate to contact us anytime. Thank you.

女 您好，這裡是湖畔電信。關於您的電話費，您似乎還沒有繳納上個月的帳單，我們將向您收取逾期罰款。很遺憾，逾期已超過十天，將酌收帳單總金額的 10%。請您盡快繳交電話費與逾期罰款。和往常一樣，您可以透過電話、電子郵件或網路繳款。如有任何疑問，請儘管隨時和我們聯絡。謝謝您。

女子提到什麼問題？
(A) 部分顧客資訊有誤。
(B) 某活動取消了。
(C) 某項商品賣光了。
(D) 逾期未繳款。

解析

獨白中提到對方上個月未繳交電話費，所以要求他支付逾期罰款（It seems that you still haven't paid last month's bill, so we have to charge you a late fee）。由此可知女子提及的問題為超過繳納期限，因此答案為 (D)。

2

M Hello. This is Feliciano Manetto, and I'm calling about an issue I am having with your website. I am trying to sign up for online banking, but I keep receiving the same error. It says that the customer information doesn't match the information on record. However, I just opened this account last week, so I am sure nothing has changed. I think maybe my name is misspelled in your system. Could you please call me back and let me know how you have my name in your records? Thanks.

男 哈囉，我是費利奇亞諾·馬奈托，我打電話給貴行，是因為我在貴行網站上遇到了問題。我正在申請網路銀行，但一直跳出相同的錯誤訊息，說我的顧客資訊與紀錄不符，可是我上週才開戶，所以我很確定沒有作過任何更改。我想可能是貴行系統把我的名字拼錯了。可否請貴行回電給我，讓我知道我在貴行紀錄上的名字嗎？謝謝。

說話者想做什麼？
(A) 確認個人資訊
(B) 取消帳戶
(C) 下訂單
(D) 要求退款

解析

獨白最後要求對方回電給自己，告知自己在紀錄上的名字為何（Could you please call me back and let me know how you have my name in your records?），因此答案為 (A)。

實戰演練 p.143

1 (A)	2 (C)	3 (B)
4 (A)	5 (D)	6 (B)

[1-3]

M Hello. It's Alexander. I was looking over the sales report that you sent me earlier this week, but something seems off. One of the sales totals from the first quarter seems unusually high. Are you sure it isn't a typo? I mean, it's way higher than any of the other items, so I think you may have typed too many zeros. Anyway, double-check the numbers and call me back when you can. Thanks.

男 您好，我是亞歷山大。我正在詳細檢閱您這週稍早前給我的銷售報告，發現有點奇怪。第一季的銷售總額當中有一項異常地高，您確定沒有打錯字嗎？我的意思是說，它比其他所有項目都高出非常多，我想您可能輸入太多個零了。總之，請再檢查一次數字是否正確，方便的話也請回電給我。謝謝。

字彙 look over 仔細檢查
something seems off 有事怪怪的
typo 打字錯誤　double-check 再次檢查

第一季	部門銷售總額
男裝	2,450.00 美元
女裝	420,000.00 美元
鞋子	9,500.00 美元
配件	8,900.00 美元

1

訊息的目的為何？
(A) 為了詢問錯誤
(B) 為了召開會議
(C) 為了確認購買
(D) 為了應徵職位

解析

當題目詢問獨白的目的時，請務必專心聆聽前半段的內容。說話者提到看過銷售報告後，發現某個金額有點怪（I was looking over the sales report that you sent me earlier this week, but something seems off），因此答案為 (A)。

2

說話者要求聽者做什麼？
(A) 提高銷售量
(B) 聯絡客戶
(C) 重新檢查部分資訊
(D) 訂購商品

解析

說話者請聽者再確認一次數字（double-check the numbers），因此答案選 (C)。

3

請看圖表。說話者有疑問的是哪個部門？
(A) 男裝
(B) 女裝
(C) 鞋子
(D) 配件

解析

說話者提到某一項的金額遠高於其他品項（it's way higher than any of the other items），明確指出問題所在。表格中，女裝的銷售金額遠高於其他品項，因此答案選 (B)。

[4-6]

M Hi. It's Peter. I'm calling about the Christmas office party we are having next week. I called the Italian restaurant that you told me about, but they said that they're completely booked on the day of our party. We need to find another caterer as soon as possible. Do you know any other businesses that can cater a party of 200 people? Who knows if we can find one in time? Anyway, call me back, and we can figure it out together. Thanks.

男 嗨，我是彼得，打給你是想問你下週辦公室聖誕派對的事。我打去你上次說的那家義大利餐廳，但他們說我們派對當天的預約都滿了。我們得盡快找到別家餐廳才行。你還知道有哪家店能承辦 200 人的派對嗎？天曉得我們能不能在時間內找到一家？無論如何，請回電給我，我們一起想辦法。謝謝。

字彙 caterer 餐飲業者　business 店家　figure out 想出

4

活動為何舉辦？
(A) 為了慶祝節日
(B) 為了促銷產品
(C) 為了慶祝榮退
(D) 為了鼓勵團隊合作

解析

前半段獨白中，說話者提到打電話來是為了下週的聖誕派對，選項中與該活動目的最為貼近的說明為 (A)。

5

關於義大利餐廳，說話者怎麼說？
(A) 非常美味。
(B) 地點便利。
(C) 菜單不合適。
(D) 沒辦法辦活動。

解析

獨白中提到，義大利餐廳表示派對當天的預約已經滿了（they said that they're completely booked on the day of our party），因此答案為 (D)。

6

說話者表示「天曉得我們能不能在時間內找到一家」，意思為何？
(A) 他對該產業不熟。
(B) 他不確定活動前是否能找到餐廳。
(C) 他想找別人幫忙辦派對。
(D) 他需要再次聯絡餐廳。

解析

「Who knows if . . . ?」的意思為「天曉得……？」、「誰知道……？」，用於表示無法肯定 if 後方的內容。

04 會議／公告 p.145

STEP 1 題型演練

1 (A)　　　2 (C)

1

根據說話者所說的內容，為何有此異動？
(A) 為了更能追蹤互動
(B) 為了方便櫃員評鑑
(C) 為了招聘更多櫃員

解析

說話者提到相關異動為登入電腦系統的方法，而該異動有助於追蹤顧客的互動內容（The goal is to help us track our customer interactions better），因此答案為 (A)。

2

聽眾被要求會議後須做什麼？
(A) 聯絡顧客
(B) 建立新的身分代碼
(C) 確認電子信箱

解析

獨白最後，說話者表示可從電子郵件中確認（Just check your email）新的個人登錄帳號，因此答案為 (C)。

STEP 2 常考用法

1 am pleased to announce / open a new branch office
2 come up with plans to increase sales
3 The goal is to help employees communicate effectively
4 have their pros and cons
5 ready to make an announcement
6 considering a new payroll system

STEP 3 聽寫練習

1 (A)　　　2 (D)

1

M Before we start today's meeting, I'd like to make an announcement. Last week, our S-Series Furniture line won the Best Modern Design Award at the International Furniture Awards in Frankfurt, Germany! I'd like to congratulate the members of the design team on their achievement. This will really help us make a name for our company, and it is a great success for all of us here. In the future, I would like the design team to work closely with the marketing team to help promote this furniture line.

男 在今天會議開始之前，我想先宣布一件事。上週，我們的 S 系列家具在德國法蘭克福國際家具大獎中贏得了最佳現代設計獎，我想為這項成就恭喜設計團隊成員。這對我們公司名譽助益真的很大，對我們的全體員工來說是一項重大的成功。在未來，我希望設計團隊和行銷團隊能緊密合作，一起提高這系列家具的銷售業績。

關於設計團隊，說話者講了什麼？
(A) 他們獲獎了。
(B) 其全體成員均為新進人員。
(C) 他們為公司省錢。
(D) 他們開發了新系統。

解析
前半段獨白中，說話者對設計團隊的成果表示祝賀（I'd like to congratulate the members of the design team on their achievement），並提及獲頒最佳現代設計獎一事，明確說出具體的成果，因此答案選 (A)。

2

M Welcome, everybody, to the Youth Support Committee. As you know, we are in the process of selecting a new project to invest in for young people in our city. As of now, we have narrowed down our options to two choices: building a new community center and opening a public pool. Both options have pros and cons, which we have discussed in previous meetings. Today, I would like you all to cast a vote for your choice between the two.

男 歡迎各位來到青年扶助委員會。你們應該都知道，我們正在挑選一項新的專案來投資我們城市的年輕人。到目前為止，我們已經把選項限縮到兩個：興建新的社區中心，或是設立公共游泳池。兩個選項各有利弊，我們上次開會時已經討論過了。今天我希望大家都能投票從中做出選擇。

說話者要求聽眾做什麼？
(A) 討論優缺點
(B) 審查文件
(C) 提名候選人
(D) 在兩個選項當中做決定

解析
獨白最後，說話者希望聽眾從兩個選項中選出一個（Today, I would like you all to cast a vote for your choice between the two），因此答案應選 (D)。

實戰演練　　　　　　　　　　　　　p.148

1 (D)	2 (B)	3 (A)
4 (A)	5 (B)	6 (B)

[1-3]

W All right, everyone, we <u>are here to discuss plans</u> for this weekend's big sale. Now, I think we should move our top-selling TV accessories <u>to the front display</u> during the sale so that customers <u>can find them easily</u>. It's <u>across from the cashier</u> and <u>next to the latest smart TVs</u>, too, so it will be easy to introduce them to customers. Remember that <u>anyone who purchases a smart TV can get a 20% discount</u> on any TV accessories they buy. In addition, all laptops and DVD players <u>will be on sale</u>, too. I want to see higher sales of them if possible.

女 好，大家，我們在這裡要討論這週末大特賣的計畫。是這樣子的，我認為在特賣期間，應該把我們最暢銷的電視周邊配件移到前方的陳列區，讓客人可以更容易找到。那個位置就在收銀台對面，也剛好在最新款智慧電視的旁邊，跟客人做介紹很方便。記得如果有人買智慧電視，可以用八折的價格加購任何他們想買的電視周邊配件。另外，所有筆電和DVD播放器也都在特賣中。如果可能的話，我希望可以看到更好的銷售業績。

字彙 **top-selling** 最暢銷的　**display** 陳列區
cashier 收銀員（衍生為「收銀台」）
the latest 最新型的　**purchase** 購買
on sale 特賣中

1
聽眾最有可能是誰？
(A) 顧客
(B) 供應商
(C) 技術人員
(D) 店員

解析

前半段獨白中，說話者表示將聽眾聚集在此的目的為討論特賣活動的計畫（we are here to discuss plans for this weekend's big sale），而討論的內容為改變陳列的位置以及提升業績，由此可知聽眾為店員，因此答案為 (D)。

2
顧客要如何才能享有電視周邊配件的折扣？
(A) 帶優惠券來用
(B) 購買智慧電視
(C) 在網路上註冊
(D) 推薦給朋友

解析

獨白中提到若購買智慧電視，可享有電視周邊配件八折的優惠（Remember that anyone who purchases a smart TV can get a 20% discount on any TV accessories they buy），因此答案為 (B)。

3
請看圖表。電視周邊配件會陳列在哪裡？
(A) 陳列區1
(B) 陳列區2
(C) 陳列區3
(D) 陳列區4

解析

獨白中提到要將電視周邊配件的陳列區移至收銀台對面、智慧電視的旁邊，為陳列區1的位置，因此答案為 (A)。

[4-6]

M Okay, one last thing before we <u>end today's meeting</u>. I want to talk about <u>the decrease in our number of international clients</u>. Last year, we had 22% <u>more orders from overseas than we have had</u> so far this year. I'm really concerned about this, and I <u>want your help with it</u>. At our next meeting, I'd like everyone to bring some ideas about how to solve this problem. Here, I'll pass around a copy of the data for you.

男 好，今天會議結束前還有一件事，我想談談海外客戶減少的情形。我們今年到目前為止的海外訂單，比去年少了22%。這真的讓我很擔心，我想要大家幫幫忙。我希望下次開會時，大家可以提出一些解決問題的想法。現在我把數據資料的影本傳下去給大家。

字彙 **decrease in** 在……方面的減少情形
client 客戶
be concerned about 對……擔憂
pass around 傳遞

4
說話者在討論什麼問題？
(A) 海外顧客減少
(B) 一名問題員工
(C) 職場多樣性不足
　　（譯註：如年齡、性別、族裔或價值觀等的多樣性）
(D) 裁員需求

解析
獨白中提及當前面臨的問題，表示與去年相比，今年海外的訂單大幅下跌（Last year, we had 22% more orders from overseas than we have had so far this year），故正確答案為 (A)。

5
說話者要求聽眾下次開會時做什麼？
(A) 提早到場
(B) 分享意見
(C) 提出銷售報告
(D) 檢討公司政策

解析
獨白中要求聽眾於下次會議中提出問題的解決方案。(B)「分享意見」，為意思最為貼近的選項，故為正確答案。

6
說話者接下來最有可能做什麼？
(A) 接顧客訂單
(B) 分發資料
(C) 開始開會
(D) 招募新人

解析
獨白最後，說話者提到要將數據資料發給各位看（I'll pass around a copy of the data for you），因此答案為 (B)。

多益實戰單字 PART 4 UNIT ❶ - ❹　　p.150

A
1 (A)　　**2** (A)　　**3** (B)　　**4** (B)　　**5** (B)

B
1 celebrate
2 local
3 misspelled
4 looking over
5 affect

C
1 Nothing is worse than
2 how difficult it is to learn
3 enjoy this chance to take
4 when you are available
5 I am calling about

05 發表／人物介紹　　p.151

STEP 1 題型演練

1 (A)　　　　**2** (B)

1
這段演說的主旨為何？
(A) 慶祝阿爾米爾先生退休
(B) 介紹講者
(C) 說明計畫

解析
獨白最後提到向 Mr. Armil（阿爾米爾先生）表達感謝之意，並祝福他退休（wish him happiness in his retirement）。這表示該段演説的目的為祝賀他退休，因此答案為 (A)。

2
阿爾米爾先生創立了什麼？
(A) 貧困家庭的庇護所
(B) 支持貧困家庭的計畫
(C) 跨國公司

解析
獨白中間提到 Mr. Armil（阿爾米爾先生）為社區擴大服務計畫的創立者，向需要處理法律問題的家庭提供協助（he was the founder of our community outreach program that helps needy families who are facing legal troubles），因此答案應選 (B)。

1 I am here to talk about
2 are delighted to present an award / Please join me
3 has been with our firm / contributed to
4 I am honored to introduce
5 began her position as the head
6 has had a great influence on

1 (B)　　　　2 (B)

1

W The next speaker I <u>would like to introduce to you</u> is Amy Spencer, who has <u>been with the company</u> for 10 years. <u>Ever since</u> she joined the company in 2008, she has been <u>working as a regional manager</u>. With her excellent <u>leadership</u> skills and <u>professional knowledge</u>, she made her branch <u>the most profitable one</u> this year. That's why she is <u>here today to share</u> her success stories and also to <u>encourage</u> us to <u>perform better</u> in our regions. I would like you to <u>welcome her with a big hand</u>.

女 我想向大家介紹的下一位演講者是艾咪・斯賓賽,她在我們公司服務十年了。從 2008 年進公司,她就一直擔任區域經理的職務。她的領導能力出色、專業知識豐富,使她的分店成為今年度收益之最,而這就是為什麼她今天來到這裡分享她的成功故事,並激勵我們這一地區工作表現的原因。請大家熱烈鼓掌歡迎她。

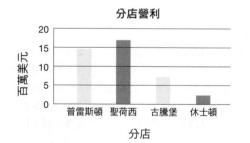

分店營利

請看圖表。斯賓塞女士負責哪家分店?
(A) 普雷斯頓
(B) 聖荷西
(C) 古騰堡
(D) 休斯頓

解析

獨白中介紹講者 Amy Spencer(艾咪・斯賓賽)所屬分店創下的獲利為今年最高(she made her branch the most profitable one this year)。圖表中顯示獲利最高的分店為 San Jose(聖荷西),因此答案為 (B)。

2

W Welcome to today's photography seminar. Please take a seat <u>at any of the computers</u>, and we will begin. Today, <u>you are going to learn</u> how to organize your photos online <u>in a more manageable way</u>. But before we begin, <u>I want to explain</u> one detail about the conference. <u>As you may already know</u>, lunch is included with the conference. <u>I will be passing out</u> free lunch coupons <u>at the end of the seminar</u>, so <u>make sure</u> you get one before you leave. You can use it at the hotel restaurant <u>any time after 12 P.M.</u>

女 歡迎蒞臨今天的攝影研討會。請挑選任何一台電腦並就座,我們馬上就要開始了。你們今天會學到怎麼樣才能更有條有理地整理網路照片。不過我們開始之前,我想先說明一件和會議有關的事項。你們可能已經知道了,這次會議有提供午餐。我會在研討會結束時發放免費餐券,所以請務必在離開前確認您有領到。這張餐券在中午 12 點過後隨時都可以在飯店餐廳使用。

聽眾被告知中午 12 點過後要做什麼?
(A) 報名參加研討
(B) 吃飯
(C) 拍照
(D) 找座位

解析

獨白中提到在 12 點過後,能在飯店餐廳內使用餐券(You can use it at the hotel restaurant any time after 12 P.M.),因此答案為 (B)。

實戰演練　　　　　　　　p.154

1 (B)	2 (C)	3 (C)
4 (A)	5 (C)	6 (D)

[1-3]

W Thank you all for joining us for the grand opening of our new location! As the store manager in charge of this branch of Derby's Music, let me be the first to welcome you all. This store is our first in Europe, and I hope to bring you the best products and provide the best service possible. To start, we are offering a free gift to everyone here today. All you have to do is subscribe to our email newsletter. You can sign up on any of the tablet computers that we have set up in the store.

女 感謝大家和我們一起慶祝新分店的盛大開幕。作為負責這間德比音樂的分店經理，讓我來搶個頭香歡迎你們的光臨。這是我們在歐洲的第一家分店，我期待能帶給你們最好的產品、提供最棒的服務。首先，我們要送給今天來到這裡的各位一個贈品。只要訂閱我們的電子報就可以拿到贈品，大家可以用我們店裡設置的任何一台平板電腦來訂閱。

字彙 location 位置　in charge of 為……負責　subscribe to 訂閱　newsletter 電子報　sign up 訂閱

1
說話者是誰？
(A) 分店長
(B) 分店經理
(C) 政治人物
(D) 投資者

解析

獨白開頭處，說話者表示自己是這家 Derby's Music（德比音樂）的分店經理，歡迎大家的光臨（As the store manager in charge of this branch of Derby's Music, let me be the first to welcome you all），表明自己的身分，因此答案為 (B)。

2
這家分店在哪裡？
(A) 北美洲
(B) 亞洲
(C) 歐洲
(D) 澳洲

解析

獨白中提到這家分店是歐洲第一家分店（This store is our first in Europe），表示該分店設在歐洲，因此答案為 (C)。

3
客人要如何才能獲得免費贈品？
(A) 撥打熱線
(B) 完成問卷
(C) 訂閱刊物
(D) 推薦給朋友

解析

獨白中提到只要來訪者訂閱電子報，皆能獲得免費贈品（we are offering a free gift to everyone here today），因此答案為 (C)。(C) 將「email newsletter」（電子報）改寫成 publication（刊物）。

[4-6]

M Good evening, everyone, and welcome to the 12th annual Architecture & Construction Achievements Awards Ceremony hosted by the Hong Kong Construction Initiative. Today, we will be announcing the winners of the following five awards: Best Design, Most Practical, Most Ecofriendly, Most Innovative, and Safest. Each category was chosen by a committee of professional designers, architects, and construction managers. The first category of the evening is Best Design, and to announce the winner, the president of the Hong Kong Construction Initiative will be here. Please join me in welcoming him on stage with a round of applause.

男 大家午安，歡迎蒞臨香港建設促進會主辦的第12屆年度建築及建設頒獎典禮。今天，我們將宣布以下五個獎項的得獎者：最佳設計獎、最實用獎、最環保獎、最創新獎以及最安全獎。每個項目均由專業設計師、建築師和工程負責人組成的委員會進行評選。今晚的第一個獎項是最佳設計獎，頒獎人是香港建設促進會主席。請和我一起以熱烈的掌聲歡迎他上台。

字彙 annual 年度的　architecture 建築　construction 建設　committee 委員會　category 類別

4

聽眾最有可能是誰？
(A) 建築師
(B) 律師
(C) 演員
(D) 警察

解析

說話者提到歡迎大家來到第 12 屆年度建築及建設頒獎典禮（welcome to the 12th annual Architecture & Construction Achievements Awards Ceremony），由此可以推測聽眾應為建築師，因此答案為 (A)。

5

典禮上將會宣布多少個獎項？
(A) 3 個
(B) 4 個
(C) 5 個
(D) 6 個

解析

獨白中提到共將頒發五個獎項（we will be announcing the winners of the following five awards），因此答案為 (C)。

6

接下來最有可能發生什麼事？
(A) 將會上餐點。
(B) 賓客將離開建築物。
(C) 電影將開播。
(D) 某人將上台。

解析

獨白中提到待會將由香港建設促進會的主席來公布獲獎者（to announce the winner, the president of the Hong Kong Construction Initiative will be here），因此答案應選 (D)。

06 觀光／展覽／參觀　　　p.156

STEP 1 題型演練

1 (B)	2 (C)

1

聽眾最有可能是誰？
(A) 顧客
(B) 遊客
(C) 士兵

解析

說話者表示自己是負責市內觀光巴士的導遊（I'll be your guide on this city bus tour today），聽眾最有可能是遊客，因此答案為 (B)。

2

說話者說不能做什麼？
(A) 在宮殿裡吃東西
(B) 在公車上提問
(C) 在行程中下車

解析

說話者表示行程途中不能任意下車（you cannot get off the bus anytime during the tour），因此答案為 (C)。

STEP 2 常考用法

1 are not allowed to take photographs
2 restore this historic building / open it to the public
3 modern art exhibit features
4 a landmark in New York City
5 Let's head over to / destination
6 buy some souvenirs at the gift shop

STEP 3 聽寫練習

1 (B)	2 (A)

1

W All right, the next part of our forest tour is going to take us into Murphy Cave. This cave system is over 150 kilometers in length, which makes it the longest one in the region. It's really an amazing wonder of nature. We will only go in about 1 kilometer on today's tour. Now, there is a species of bat that lives here, and it is very sensitive to light. So flash photography is not permitted within the cave. Normal photos are fine, but you must turn off the flash.

女 好，我們森林之旅的下一站是墨菲洞穴。這個洞穴系統全長超過 150 公里，是當地最長的一個，真的是大自然的奇蹟。我們今天的行程只會進到約一公里深的地方。還有，有一種蝙蝠棲息在此，牠們對光非常敏感，因此山洞中禁止用閃光燈攝影。一般的拍照是沒關係的，不過大家得把閃光燈關掉。

說話者說不能做什麼？
(A) 餵食動物
(B) 用閃光燈拍照
(C) 進入山洞
(D) 觸摸蝙蝠

解析

最後一段獨白中，說話者表示蝙蝠對光非常敏感，禁止使用閃光燈拍照（So flash photography is not permitted within the cave），因此答案應選 (B)。

2

M Welcome to the Van Dijk Brewery tour. Let's start today with some information about the company. Did you know that Van Dijk beer is served in more than 30 different countries around the world? Well, today, you are going to see how we make our beers. You will see the major processes such as malting and fermenting. You will also see where we bottle and ship the beers. And at the end of the tour, we will even offer you the chance to taste three of our most popular beers for free. Follow me this way, please.

男 歡迎參加范迪克釀酒廠之旅。首先我們先來認識一下這家公司。你們知道范迪克啤酒在全世界超過30個國家都有販售嗎？嗯，今天你們將會了解我們啤酒的製作方式。你們會看到麥芽處理和發酵等主要製程，也會看到啤酒裝瓶和裝運的場所。到導覽的尾聲，你們甚至有機會免費試飲任三種我們最受歡迎的啤酒。請跟我走這邊。

范迪克釀酒廠之旅	
第一區	啤酒試飲
第二區	麥芽處理
第三區	發酵
第四區	裝瓶及裝運

請看圖表。聽眾到導覽的尾聲時會去哪一區？
(A) 第一區
(B) 第二區
(C) 第三區
(D) 第四區

解析

獨白中提到在導覽的最後，會提供免費試飲啤酒的機會（at the end of the tour, we will even offer you the chance to taste three of our most popular beers for free）。根據表格中的內容，會在第一區試飲啤酒，因此答案為 (A)。

1 (B)	**2** (A)	**3** (D)
4 (C)	**5** (D)	**6** (A)

[1-3]

M And this completes our tour of the museum. Thank you all for joining us today, and I apologize again for your not being able to see the native history section because of construction. If you bring your ticket back after May 1, you can see the newly renovated native history exhibit free of charge. On your way out, I suggest stopping by the gift shop. It has a great selection of souvenirs and postcards. You can even mail a postcard directly from the shop for free.

男 我們博物館的參觀就到這裡結束。感謝大家今天的參與，我也再次說聲抱歉，原住民歷史展區因為施工沒辦法讓你們參觀。如果你們在5月1日過後帶著門票回來，就可以免費參觀剛整修好的原住民歷史展區。你們離開的時候，我建議你們順路去禮品店逛逛，那裡有各種紀念品和明信片，大家甚至可以直接從店裡免費寄明信片。

字彙 apologize 道歉　native 原住民
construction 施工
renovated 整修完成的　exhibit 展示會
free of charge 免收費　stop by 順便造訪
souvenir 紀念品

1
這段說明發生在哪裡？
(A) 公車上
(B) 博物館內
(C) 工廠內
(D) 劇院內

解析

獨白開頭處提到博物館參觀到此結束（this completes our tour of the museum），因此答案選 (B) 博物館內。

2
關於原住民歷史展區，說明中指出什麼？
(A) 正在整修中。
(B) 從博物館撤掉了。
(C) 向來都免費。
(D) 是該建築的私人空間。

PART 4
06 觀光／展覽／參觀

89

解析

獨白中提到 5 月 1 日後，可以免費參觀整修完畢的原住民歷史展區（If you bring your ticket back after May 1, you can see the newly renovated native history exhibit free of charge）。由此可以推測目前該展區正在整修，因此答案為 (A)。

3

說話者建議聽眾做什麼？
(A) 上傳照片到社群媒體
(B) 訂閱電子報
(C) 穿過花園小徑離開
(D) 參觀禮品店

解析

說話者建議聽眾前往禮品店（I suggest stopping by the gift shop），因此答案為 (D)。

[4-6]

W If you all take a look to your left, you will see the Stanley Diner. Opened in 1909, this family restaurant is one of the most beloved establishments in our city. No trip to our city is complete without a visit, so we are going to have lunch there tomorrow. For now, let's continue our walking tour down to the docks. There, we can learn a bit about the history of the fishing industry here in Springfield and how it has grown into the nation's third biggest seafood market. You will also have about an hour of free time to explore the market by yourself.

女 看向你的左手邊，你會看到史丹利小吃。這間家庭餐廳在 1909 年開張，是我們城市裡非常受歡迎的一家店。到我們城市玩，要是沒吃過這家就不算完美，所以我們明天會在那裡吃午餐。現在讓我們繼續朝著碼頭走。在那裡，我們可以了解一些有關春田市的漁業史，以及它成長為國內第三大魚市場的契機。你們還有大約一小時的自由時間，可以自行探索市場。

字彙 take a look to 看一下　beloved 被喜愛的
dock 碼頭　industry 產業

4

說話者最有可能是誰？
(A) 服務生
(B) 漁夫
(C) 導遊
(D) 節目主持人

解析

整段獨白的內容為針對旅遊景點的導覽，因此答案為 (C)。

5

說話者說：「到我們城市玩，要是沒吃過這家就不算完美」，意思為何？
(A) 某個地點沒有很多人知道。
(B) 某個地點的競爭很激烈。
(C) 有些人想要關掉某家店。
(D) 它是這座城市的重要地點。

解析

將引號內的句子意譯出來，意思為「若未造訪（此處），便稱不上來過我們城市旅遊」，也就是此處為該城市必去不可的景點，因此答案為 (D)。

6

說話者說明天會發生什麼事？
(A) 聽眾將在著名餐廳吃午餐。
(B) 聽眾將參觀海鮮市場。
(C) 碼頭將有船舶展。
(D) 受歡迎的公園裡將有表演。

解析

說話者提到明天將於那裡享用午餐（we are going to have lunch there tomorrow），而那裡指的是前方提及的餐廳 Stanley Diner（史丹利小吃），因此答案為 (A)。

07 公共場所告知／通知 p.161

STEP 1 題型演練

1 (A)　　　　2 (B)

1

根據廣播內容，聽眾在游泳池關閉後能做什麼？
(A) 使用 SPA 池
(B) 按個摩
(C) 上游泳課

解析

獨白中提到游泳池暫停使用期間，仍能使用熱水池、SPA 池和躺椅（You may still use the hot tub and spa as well as the lounge chairs），因此答案為 (A)。

2

說話者建議泳客做什麼？
(A) 休息一下
(B) 吃點零食
(C) 享受熱水池

解析

說話者建議在游泳池進行清潔期間，可以到販賣部購買小吃或冷飲享用（We recommend taking this chance to visit the concession stand to have a snack or to enjoy a cool drink），因此答案為 (B)。選項將「have a snack」（吃小吃）改寫為「grab a bite to eat」（吃點零食）。

STEP 2 常考用法

1 sorry for any inconvenience
2 will be closed for safety reasons
3 The train bound for / will be arriving
4 turn off your mobile phones / performance begins
5 celebrate our grand opening / special offers
6 will be temporarily closed due to regular cleaning

STEP 3 聽寫練習

1 (A)　　　 2 (D)

1

M Good afternoon, passengers, and welcome aboard the commuter bus bound for Chicago. Our trip is scheduled to take 1 hour and 30 minutes. However, because of roadside construction, we expect that the roads will be more backed up than usual. Our arrival time will likely be delayed by about 30 minutes, so please keep that in mind. You can use the free Wi-Fi provided on our bus to email or message anyone that needs to be updated about your schedule. We apologize for any inconvenience that this delay may cause. Thank you.

男 各位乘客午安，歡迎搭乘開往芝加哥的通勤巴士。車程預計一個半小時，然而由於路邊施工的關係，我們預期道路會比平常更加堵塞。抵達時間可能會延誤大約 30 分鐘，還請各位留意。您可以使用我們巴士內提供的免費無線網路，來寄電子郵件或簡訊給需要知道您行程更動的對象。對於延誤可能造成的任何不便，我們深表歉意。謝謝您。

根據說話者所說的內容，公車為什麼會延誤？
(A) 因為有施工
(B) 因為公車出發得晚
(C) 因為要臨時停車
(D) 因為須另外加油

解析

獨白中提到由於道路施工，預估交通會比平常更為堵塞（because of roadside construction, we expect that the roads will be more backed up than usual），因此答案為 (A)。

2

W Ladies and gentlemen, welcome to the Fox Theater. Tonight's show, *The Story of a Boy*, will begin shortly. We would like to remind you to turn off your mobile phones to prepare for the show. We would also like to ask you to refrain from taking any photos or videos during the show. After the show, the cast will be available for photos in the lobby free of charge. We appreciate your cooperation and hope you enjoy the show.

女 各位女士先生，歡迎蒞臨福斯劇院。今晚的表演《男孩故事》即將開演。開演前，我們想提醒您關閉手機，也請您避免於演出期間拍照或錄影。表演結束後，演員將在大廳等候，各位可免費跟演員拍照。我們感謝您的配合，並希望您喜歡我們的表演。

廣播的地點為何？
(A) 書店
(B) 賣場
(C) 博物館
(D) 劇院

解析

說話者表示歡迎來到 Fox Theater（福斯劇院）（welcome to the Fox Theater），由此可知是劇院裡的廣播。

實戰演練 p.164

1 (D)	2 (C)	3 (C)
4 (B)	5 (B)	6 (D)

[1-3]

M Attention, travelers. Due to unsafe conditions caused by heavy snowfall, the 9 P.M. Bard Airline flight to Moscow has been delayed until tomorrow morning at 11 A.M. We regret any inconvenience this may cause you. Please find your way to the nearest Bard Airline counter to receive details about the newly rescheduled flight. As a token of our sincerest apologies, you can also receive a voucher for a free night at one of the airport hotels. Again, we are sorry for the delay and thank you for flying with Bard Airlines.

男 各位旅客請注意，由於大雪容易導致意外，巴德航空晚間 9 點飛往莫斯科的班機已延到明天上午 11 點起飛。我們對於可能造成的不便深感抱歉。請您前往離您最近的巴德航空櫃檯取得最新的航班時間資訊。為表達我們最誠摯的歉意，您將獲得一張免費住宿券，可在這裡任何一家機場飯店留宿一晚。我們再次為延誤致上歉意，並感謝您選擇搭乘巴德航空。

字彙 condition 情況
　　　reschedule 重新安排……的時間
　　　sincere 誠摯的　voucher 兌換券

1
根據廣播內容，時程為什麼更改？
(A) 乘客太多。
(B) 另一架班機必須先離開。
(C) 有些行李遺失了。
(D) 天候不佳。

解析

獨白中提到由於大雪的關係，產生安全上的疑慮，班機將延遲起飛（Due to unsafe conditions caused by heavy snowfall, the 9 P.M. Bard Airline flight to Moscow has been delayed until tomorrow morning at 11 A.M.），因此答案為 (D)。選項將獨白中的「heavy snowfalls」（大雪）改寫成「bad weather」（天候不佳）。

2
說話者表示旅客可以獲得什麼？
(A) 座艙升等
(B) 免費手提行李袋
(C) 飯店房間兌換券
(D) 餐點

解析

獨白中提到將提供機場飯店的免費住宿券（you can also receive a voucher for a free night at one of the airport hotels），因此答案為 (C)。

3
旅客何時可出發前往莫斯科？
(A) 今晚 9 點
(B) 今晚 11 點
(C) 明早 11 點
(D) 明晚 9 點

解析

獨白中提到班機將延至明天上午 11 點起飛（until tomorrow morning at 11 A.M.），因此答案為 (C)。

[4-6]

W Good evening, mall guests. I would like to remind you all that Pamela's Sporting Goods is opening its doors for the first time today, and it is having a special event to celebrate. Today only, all customers can receive a free tote bag with the purchase of a pair of tennis shoes. In addition, the store will be giving a free lesson on how to maintain your sports equipment during winter. You can find Pamela's Sporting Goods on the first floor in the east wing of the mall.

女 各位賣場來賓晚安。我想提醒大家，潘蜜拉體育用品店今天首度開幕，並推出特別慶祝活動。貴賓如果購買一雙網球鞋將獲贈手提袋，只有今天限定。另外，店家也會提供免費課程，教您在冬天保養運動裝備。潘蜜拉體育用品店位於本購物中心東側的一樓，歡迎您的蒞臨。

字彙 remind 提醒　celebrate 慶祝
　　　purchase 購買　maintain 保養
　　　equipment 裝備

4
關於潘蜜拉體育用品店，說話者說了什麼？
(A) 該店販賣二手體育用品。
(B) 今天是該店營業首日。
(C) 該店剛局部整修完。
(D) 該店目前換人經營。

解析

獨白開頭處，說話者表示商店於今日開幕（Pamela's Sporting Goods is opening its doors for the first time today），表示今天為開幕第一天，因此答案為 (B)。

5

顧客如果購買網球鞋，將可免費獲得什麼？

(A) 鞋帶
(B) 袋子
(C) 運動毛巾
(D) 運動裝備

解析

獨白中提到所有購買網球鞋的顧客，將獲贈免費的手提袋（all customers can receive a free tote bag with the purchase of a pair of tennis shoes），因此答案為 (B)。

6

根據廣播內容，顧客在特別活動時可以做什麼？

(A) 購買稀有收藏品
(B) 獲得大幅折扣
(C) 簽署會員合約
(D) 免費上課

解析

獨白中提到針對冬季如何保養運動裝備，將開設免費教學課程（the store will be giving a free lesson on how to maintain your sports equipment during winter），因此答案為 (D)。

多益實戰單字 PART 4 UNIT 05 - 07 p.166

A

1 (A)　　**2** (B)　　**3** (B)　　**4** (A)　　**5** (A)

B

1 honored
2 landmark
3 features
4 complimentary
5 influence

C

1 truly appreciate your cooperation
2 has been with the company
3 The train bound for Oxford
4 is scheduled to take
5 allowed to take photographs

PART 1

1 (C)　　**2** (A)　　**3** (B)

PART 2

4 (B)　　**5** (A)　　**6** (B)　　**7** (A)　　**8** (A)
9 (B)　　**10** (B)　　**11** (C)　　**12** (B)　　**13** (A)
14 (B)　　**15** (A)　　**16** (A)　　**17** (A)

PART 3

18 (A)　　**19** (D)　　**20** (B)　　**21** (A)　　**22** (B)
23 (C)　　**24** (A)　　**25** (B)　　**26** (D)　　**27** (C)
28 (B)　　**29** (C)　　**30** (A)　　**31** (B)　　**32** (B)
33 (A)　　**34** (B)　　**35** (C)

PART 4

36 (C)　　**37** (A)　　**38** (B)　　**39** (D)　　**40** (B)
41 (A)　　**42** (B)　　**43** (B)　　**44** (A)　　**45** (C)
46 (D)　　**47** (B)　　**48** (D)　　**49** (B)　　**50** (B)

PART 1

1

(A) A man is putting on a tie.
(B) A woman is using her laptop.
(C) A man is raising his hand.
(D) People are seated around a table.

(A) 一名男子正在打領帶。
(B) 一名女子正在用她的筆電。
(C) 一名男子正舉起他的手。
(D) 人們圍著一張桌子而坐。

解析

(C) 描寫一名男子把手舉起來的動作，故為正確答案。
(A) 中的「put on」指的是穿衣服的動作，因此不適合作為答案；照片中並未出現筆電或桌子，因此 (B) 和 (D) 亦不是答案。

字彙 **put on** 穿上、戴上（衣物）　**laptop** 筆電

2

(A) Cars have been parked.
(B) Vehicles are being towed away.
(C) The parking structure is being cleaned.
(D) Some cars are being washed.

(A) 車子停放著。
(B) （某人）正把車輛拖走。
(C) （某人）正在打掃立體停車場。
(D) （某人）正在洗幾台車。

解析

照片中可以看見車輛停放在巷內，因此答案為 (A)。
而 (B)、(C)、(D) 皆使用現在進行式被動語態，但照
片中並未出現人物，因此皆不適合作為答案。

字彙 tow 拖吊　parking structure 立體停車場

3

(A) They are marching in a ceremony.
(B) They are coming down the stairs.
(C) The stairs are being polished.
(D) There is a fence at the top of the stairs.

(A) 他們正在典禮中齊步向前走。
(B) 他們正在下樓梯。
(C) （某人）正把樓梯擦亮。
(D) 樓梯頂端有一道柵欄。

解析

照片中兩名男女正在下樓梯，描述內容最接近的選項
為 (B)，故為正確答案。(A) 當中 marching 的意思為
「（齊步）前進」，但他們並非在典禮（ceremony）
上行走，因此答案不能選 (A)；照片內沒有人在把
樓梯擦亮（are being polished），也沒有出現柵欄
（fence），因此 (C) 和 (D) 皆不是答案。

字彙 march（齊步）前進　ceremony 典禮

PART 2

4

When is the deadline for the proposal?
(A) The project is not known.
(B) Sue has the schedule.
(C) It's about the construction.

計畫書的截止日期是何時？
(A) 專案內容不詳。
(B) 蘇有時程表。
(C) 內容是跟建設有關。

解析

本題詢問繳交計畫書的期限。(B) 回答 Sue（蘇）有
時程表，故為正確答案。雖然 (A) 和 (C) 的內容與
proposal（計畫書）有所關聯，但是皆為答非所問。

字彙 deadline 截止期限　proposal 計畫書

5

Which conference would you like to participate in?
(A) The one about marketing.
(B) I don't want to give a speech.
(C) Seems like a long time ago.

你想參加哪一場研討會？
(A) 關於行銷的那場。
(B) 我不想發表演說。
(C) 看來好像是很久以前。

解析

本題詢問對方想參加的研討會。(A) 回答有關行銷的
研討會，故為正確答案。題目並非請對方演講，因此
(B) 不適合作為答案；(C) 提及過去，也不適合作為答
案。

字彙 participate in 參加
　　give a speech 發表演說

6

Where can I put these new shelves?
(A) They are well organized.
(B) Why don't we put them in the corner?
(C) We need to get new ones.

這些新的架子要放在哪裡?
(A) 它們排得井然有序。
(B) 我們何不把它們放在角落?
(C) 我們需要買新的。

解析

本題詢問新的架子要放在哪裡。(B) 提出建議,故為正確答案。(A) 表示都已經整理完畢、(C) 表示應該買新的,皆不適合作為答案。

字彙 organize 安排

7

Did you contact the technical support team?
(A) Yes, they are on their way.
(B) I am not a technical expert.
(C) Of course, you do.

你和技術支援團隊聯絡了嗎?
(A) 有,他們正在過來的路上。
(B) 我不是技術專家。
(C) 當然好,請這樣做。

解析

本題詢問是否已經聯絡技術支援團隊。(A) 表示他們在路上了,故為正確答案。(B) 僅重複使用 technical (技術的),但並非答案;(C) 的內容與題目無關。

字彙 be on one's way (某人)去……的途中

8

Who is in charge of the Promotions Department?
(A) It is probably Mr. Williams.
(B) I wasn't sure about it.
(C) He looked okay with me.

誰是宣傳部的負責人?
(A) 有可能是威廉斯先生。
(B) 我不確定。
(C) 我覺得他看起來不錯。

解析

本題詢問誰是宣傳部的負責人。(A) 直接告知負責人為 Mr. Williams (威廉斯先生),故為正確答案。(B)為過去式,時態不適當;(C) 則是答非所問。

字彙 in charge of 負責……

9

How can I get to the nearest airport?
(A) It is so hard to get tickets.
(B) There is an express train to it.
(C) You'd better leave early.

我該怎麼去最近的機場?
(A) 票很難買到。
(B) 有特快車可以到。
(C) 你最好早點離開。

解析

本題詢問如何前往最近的機場。(B) 回答有特快車(express train),故為正確答案。(A) 表示票很難買、(C) 表示建議早點離開,皆與前往機場的方法無關,因此不適合作為答案。

字彙 express train 特快車

10

Mr. Yang is pleased with the survey results, isn't he?
(A) No, we didn't do it.
(B) Yes, he found them satisfactory.
(C) I am afraid so.

楊先生很滿意調查結果,不是嗎?
(A) 不,我們沒做。
(B) 是的,他發現結果很令人滿意。
(C) 恐怕是這樣。

解析

本題為附加問句,詢問第三者 Mr. Yang(楊先生)對調查結果是否滿意。(B) 給予正面答覆,故為正確答案。雖然 (C) 也屬於正面答覆,但是使用「I am afraid」開頭,表示是不好的事,不符合題意。

字彙 survey 調查 **satisfactory** 令人滿意的

11

Didn't we hit our sales targets this year?
(A) Yes, it's already full.
(B) They were from the team.
(C) Actually, they were higher than we had expected.

我們不是達成今年的銷售目標了嗎?
(A) 是的,已經滿了。
(B) 來自團隊。
(C) 事實上,比我們預期的還高。

解析

本題詢問今年是否有達成銷售目標。(C) 回答比預期更高,故為正確答案。

字彙 **hit a target** 擊中目標

12

Will you be free for a company dinner on Friday?

(A) A lot of delicious food.

(B) I won't miss it.

(C) No, I haven't seen it.

你週五有空參加公司的晚宴嗎？

(A) 很多美味的食物。

(B) 我不會錯過。

(C) 不，我沒看到。

解析

本題詢問週五能否參加公司晚宴。(B) 表示一定會參加，故為正確答案。「I won't miss it」意思為「我不會錯過」，可以解釋為「一定會參加」。

13

Do you happen to know where we keep the color paper?

(A) Ask Carol.

(B) We are out of time.

(C) It didn't happen.

你知道我們把色紙放在哪裡嗎？

(A) 問一下卡蘿。

(B) 我們沒時間了。

(C) 沒有發生。

解析

本題詢問色紙擺放的位置。(A) 要求詢問 Carol（卡蘿），採間接回答的方式，故為正確答案。(B) 故意使用「out of」，意圖使人與「run out of」產生混淆，並非表示「用完」的意思。

字彙 **Do you happen to know . . . ?**

你知道……嗎？

out of time 沒時間了

14

Why did they cancel the promotional event?

(A) They were not concerned about it.

(B) There were not enough funds in the budget.

(C) In order to boost sales.

他們為什麼取消促銷活動？

(A) 他們不關心。

(B) 預算的資金不夠。

(C) 為了提升業績。

解析

本題詢問取消促銷活動的理由。(B) 回答「預算不夠」，故為正確答案。(A) 使用 concern（關心），僅與 cancel（取消）的發音相近，但並非答案；(C)「boost sales」（提升業績）僅與「promotional sales」（促銷活動）有所關聯，為答題陷阱。

字彙 **promotional event** 促銷活動

be concerned about 關心　**budget** 預算

boost 提高

15

Can I get you anything to drink?

(A) That would be great.

(B) All I had was a glass of water.

(C) They liked it, too.

要不要我幫你拿點喝的來？

(A) 如果可以就太好了。

(B) 我只有一杯水。

(C) 他們也喜歡。

解析

本題的意思為詢問對方「需要喝點什麼嗎」。(A) 給予正面答覆，故為正確答案。(B) 和 (C) 的內容皆不符合題意。

16

Would you like to take a guided tour or travel on your own?

(A) I prefer a packaged tour.

(B) I have my own car.

(C) Suit yourself.

你想要有導遊帶，還是自助行？

(A) 我比較喜歡套裝行程。

(B) 我自己有車。

(C) 請自便。

解析

本題詢問要選擇套裝行程還是獨自旅行。(A) 表示套裝行程比較好，故為正確答案。

字彙 **suit yourself** 請自便

17

Are you going to rent a car while you are there?

(A) Public transportation would be better.

(B) I don't have a car.

(C) Well, it's the first time.

你待在那裡的期間要租車嗎？
(A) 我比較想使用大眾運輸工具。
(B) 我沒有車。
(C) 嗯，這是第一次。

解析

本題詢問是否要租車。(A) 直譯為「搭乘大眾運輸工具比較好」，代表說話者比起租車，更想要使用大眾運輸工具，故為正確答案。(B) 表示沒有車子、(C) 表示這是第一次，皆與題目內容無關。

字彙 rent 租用　public transportation 大眾運輸

PART 3

[18-20]

W　I am calling because I will be arriving in New York next Tuesday, and I would like to make an appointment to see you. I would like to talk to you about the new product that we launched last month.

M　Good. What day would be good for you? Next week, I am kind of busy with other things.

W　How about Wednesday or Thursday?

M　Wednesday is no good for me, but on Thursday, I think I can squeeze you in late in the afternoon.

W　Yeah, that would be great. What about 5 o'clock? Is that okay?

M　Good. I will send my driver to pick you up at around 4:30 then.

女　我打電話來，是因為我下週二會到紐約，我想要跟你約見面。我想和你談談我們上個月推出的新產品。

男　好的。你哪一天方便？下週我有其他事，會有點忙。

女　週三或週四如何？

男　我週三不行。不過如果是週四，我想下午晚一點我可以擠出一些時間給你。

女　好，那太好了。5 點怎麼樣，可以嗎？

男　好。那我會派我的司機大約 4 點半去接你。

字彙 appointment（會面的）約定　launch 推出
squeeze 擠

18

女子為什麼想和男子見面？
(A) 為了討論他們的新產品
(B) 為了安排會議的時間
(C) 為了推出一項新產品
(D) 為出差作準備

解析

女子表示想與男子見面談談上個月推出的新產品（I would like to talk to you about the new product that we launched last month），因此答案為 (A)。

19

談話的人何時會見面？
(A) 週一
(B) 週二
(C) 週三
(D) 週四

解析

男子表示可與女子安排於週四下午碰面（on Thursday, I think I can squeeze you in late in the afternoon），因此答案為 (D)。

20

男子說他會做什麼？
(A) 訂機票
(B) 派車去接女子
(C) 打電話給生產部主管
(D) 安排下週的行程

解析

男子表示要派司機過去接女子（I will send my driver to pick you at around 4:30 then），因此答案應選 (B)。

[21-23]

M　I am calling from room 342. I haven't been getting any hot water in the shower all day today.

W　Oh, I am so sorry for the inconvenience. Actually, we are already aware of that problem since some of the other guests on your floor are experiencing the same problem.

M　When do you think it will be resolved?

W　I think it will be fixed within a few hours. But if you need hot water right now, you can use the community shower by the swimming pool.

男 我這裡是 342 號房。我今天一整天浴室都沒有熱水可以用。

女 噢，很抱歉造成您的不便。事實上，我們已經知道那個問題了，因為您那層樓的有些房客也遇到相同的狀況。

男 那你們覺得問題何時能解決呢？

女 我想幾個小時內就會修好。但如果您現在就需要熱水，您可以先使用游泳池旁的公用淋浴間。

字彙 inconvenience 不便　aware 知道的
resolve 解決　community 公用的

21
女子最有可能是誰？
(A) 飯店職員
(B) 商店經理
(C) 技術人員
(D) 飯店顧客

解析
男子向女子提出在飯店內碰到的不便之處（inconvenience），由此可知女子應為飯店職員。

22
討論的問題為何？
(A) 淋浴間故障。
(B) 沒有熱水。
(C) 房間太吵。
(D) 那一層樓有太多客人。

解析
男子表示自己的房間沒有熱水（I haven't been getting any hot water in the shower all day today），因此答案為 (B)。

23
男子被建議做什麼？
(A) 享受在游泳池的時光
(B) 休息一下
(C) 使用游泳池旁邊的淋浴間
(D) 立刻退房

解析
女子告訴男子，若男子需要使用熱水，可以到游泳池旁的公共淋浴間（if you need hot water right now, you can use the community shower by the swimming pool），因此答案為 (C)。

[24-26]

W1 Okay, the next item on our agenda is the international technology convention that we will be hosting next year. We need to start planning, and I think we should find a location as soon as possible. Does anyone have any suggestions?

M We held it at the Terrace Hotel the last time. I think that worked out very well. Why don't we hold it there again this time?

W1 Well, that's not a bad idea. Janet, can you contact the manager at the Terrace Hotel to make a reservation?

W2 I already tried that, and the person there said that hotel management has decided to stop hosting conferences.

M Really? That's too bad. What should we do?

W1 I heard that the city convention center has just reopened after completing renovations.

M I will contact someone there right away and see if it is available.

女1 好，我們議程上的下一個事項，是有關我們明年主辦的國際科技大會。我們得開始規劃，而且我想我們要盡快找到場地。有沒有誰有任何建議？

男 上一次我們辦在泰倫斯飯店，我覺得結果非常棒。我們何不這一次也在那裡辦？

女1 嗯，這建議不錯。珍奈特，你可以和泰倫斯飯店的經理聯絡預訂一下嗎？

女2 我已經聯絡過了，但他們說飯店高層已經決定不再承辦會議了。

男 真的嗎？真糟糕。那我們該怎麼辦？

女1 我聽說市立會議中心整修完成後，剛剛重新開幕了。

男 我立刻和他們聯絡看看有沒有檔期。

字彙 item 項目　agenda 議程
work out 結果是……　renovation 整修

24
這段談話最有可能發生在哪裡？
(A) 會議室
(B) 飯店
(C) 會議中心
(D) 禮堂

解析
參與對話的人正針對國際科技大會的場地進行討論，由此可知對話地點在 (A) 會議室。

25

男子說「我覺得結果非常棒」，意思為何？

(A) 某個計畫結果輕鬆完成。

(B) 先前的一個活動很成功。

(C) 他們為一個即將到來的活動找到一個好場地。

(D) 辦公室整修進度超前。

解析

男子提到上次在 Terrace Hotel（泰倫斯飯店）舉行，當時辦得相當不錯（We held it at the Terrace Hotel the last time. I think that worked out very well）。由此段話可知題目引用的句子指的是「先前的活動辦得很成功」，因此答案為 (B)。

26

男子接下來可能會做什麼？

(A) 召開會議討論一個活動

(B) 取消他們在市立會議中心的預訂

(C) 確認在泰倫斯飯店的預訂

(D) 聯絡會議中心洽談一個活動

解析

女子表示 Terrace Hotel（泰倫斯飯店）不再提供場地舉辦會議，接著向男子提及另一項資訊：市立會議中心已整修完畢並重新開幕。而後男子表示會聯絡那裡的員工，確認是否可以使用（I will contact someone there right away and see if it is available），因此答案為 (D)。

[27-29]

M1 Lena has been working here for six months now, and she just finished her probationary period. Michael, how do you feel about offering her a full-time contract?

M2 Well, I am not sure about it. Here in this report, it says she was late for work several times.

W I don't think that is very important. As far as I know, she had good reasons for being late. She has been doing a great job, and she also has some great ideas.

M2 If that's how you feel, I don't have a problem with hiring her full time. I think she is a great assistant, too.

M1 Well, then I think we can offer her a full-time position. I will call her right away and deliver the good news.

男 1 莉娜已經來工作六個月了，她剛剛才結束試用期。麥可，你覺得和她簽全職契約如何？

男 2 嗯，我不確定該不該這麼做。這份報告裡說她遲到了好幾次。

女 我覺得那還好。就我所知，她遲到都有充分的理由。她的工作表現優異，也有一些很棒的點子。

男 2 如果你這麼覺得，那我對全職僱用她沒有意見。我也覺得她是一位很棒的助理。

男 1 嗯，那麼我想我們可以給她一個全職的職位。我馬上就打電話給她，告訴她這個好消息。

字彙 probationary 試用的　as long as 只要……

27

這段談話的主旨為何？

(A) 進行面試

(B) 修訂公司政策

(C) 提供某人全職工作

(D) 安排出差

解析

對話開頭，男子提出讓 Lena（莉娜）轉為全職的想法，並詢問其他人的意見，因此答案為 (C)。

28

關於莉娜，女子說了什麼？

(A) 她不準時。

(B) 她的表現一直都很好。

(C) 她和同事相處愉快。

(D) 她對這個工作不感興趣。

解析

女子表示 Lena（莉娜）工作表現優異，也常常提出很好的點子（She has been doing a great job, and she also has some great ideas），因此答案為 (B)。

29

男子將如何聯絡莉娜？

(A) 透過電子郵件

(B) 透過信件

(C) 透過電話

(D) 親自去找她

解析

對話最後，男子表示要打電話給 Lena（莉娜）告訴她這個好消息（I will call her right away and deliver the good news），因此答案為 (C)。

[30-32]

W Excuse me. What is the best way to get to the nearest shopping mall?

M You can either take a taxi or one of the free shuttles. I suggest you take one of them. It is rush hour now, so a taxi will cost you a lot.

W Good. Thanks. I will try that then. Where can I get some information about the shuttles?

M The schedule is over there near the counter. Oh, by the way, please note that the green shuttle is temporarily out of service at the moment.

女 不好意思，請問到最近的購物中心最好的方式是什麼？

男 您可以搭計程車，或搭免費接駁車的其中一路。我建議您搭接駁車，現在是尖峰時間，所以搭計程車會花很多錢。

女 好的，謝謝，那我試試接駁車。我要去哪裡看接駁車的資訊呢？

男 時刻表在靠近櫃檯那邊。噢，對了，請留意綠線接駁車目前暫時停駛。

字彙 shuttle 接駁車　rush hour 交通尖峰時間
　　 temporarily 暫時地

接駁車名稱	終點站	行車間隔
藍線	遊樂園	每30分鐘一班
紅線	大C購物中心	每60分鐘一班
黃線	火車站	每30分鐘一班
綠線	大C購物中心	每20分鐘一班

30

女子詢問男子什麼事？

(A) 去購物中心的最佳方式
(B) 避開交通尖峰時間的最佳方式
(C) 如何預約接駁車服務
(D) 如何節省交通費用

解析

女子詢問男子如何前往最近的購物中心（What is the best way to get to the nearest shopping mall?），因此答案為 (A)。

31

男子為什麼說計程車不是個好選擇？

(A) 因為通常都很貴
(B) 因為現在車很多
(C) 因為計程車沒有開到她所在的大樓
(D) 因為無法保證前來載客的時間

解析

男子表示現在是尖峰時間、交通量大，搭乘計程車可能得花很多錢（It is rush hour now, so a taxi will cost you a lot），因此答案應選 (B)。

32

請看圖表。女子有可能搭哪一路接駁車？

(A) 藍線
(B) 紅線
(C) 黃線
(D) 綠線

解析

根據表格，搭乘紅線和綠線公車皆能抵達購物中心。但在對話中，男子表示綠線公車暫時停駛（the green shuttle is temporarily out of service at the moment），因此答案為 (B)。

[33-35]

M Hi, Jess. I am making a reservation for our trip to Buenos Aires. Do you have a hotel to stay at in mind?

W This time, I would like to stay at a place where transportation is more convenient.

M I am so with you. The last time we went there, it was good that we stayed near the shopping mall and a nice park, but it was a little inconvenient to get around.

W Is there a hotel that suits our needs?

M There is one right next to the subway station.

W That one looks good. Yes, we should reserve rooms at that one.

男 嗨，潔絲，我正在預訂我們去布宜諾斯艾利斯的旅程。你有想住的飯店嗎？

女 這次我想住在一個交通比較方便的地方。

男 我也這麼想。我們上次去時，飯店附近有購物中心和舒服的公園，雖然很棒，但要去四處走走也有點不方便。

女 有符合我們需求的飯店嗎？

男 有一間就在地鐵站旁邊。

女 那一間看起來很好。好，我們就預訂那間飯店的房間吧。

字彙 make a reservation 預訂
　　 inconvenient 不方便的
　　 get around 四處走動

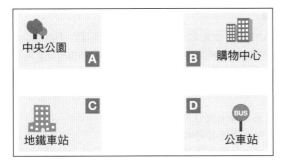

中央公園 A
購物中心 B
地鐵車站 C
公車站 D BUS

33

談話的人主要在討論什麼？

(A) 他們在旅程中要住在哪裡

(B) 要去哪裡度假

(C) 度假時要做什麼

(D) 如何去布宜諾斯艾利斯

解析

男子表示他正在預訂去布宜諾斯艾利斯的旅程，詢問女子是否有想住的飯店（I am making a reservation for our trip to Buenos Aires. Do you have a hotel to stay at in mind?），因此答案為 (A)。

34

關於他們的前一次旅行，男子說了什麼？

(A) 食物很難吃。

(B) 很難去別的地方走走。

(C) 太擁擠了。

(D) 購物中心很遠。

解析

男子表示上次入住的飯店不太方便四處走走（it was a little inconvenient to get around），因此答案為 (B)。

35

請看圖表。談話的人有可能會住在哪裡？

(A) A

(B) B

(C) C

(D) D

解析

對話最後，男子表示地鐵站旁邊有間飯店（There is one right next to the subway station），而後女子表示要預訂那間飯店（we should reserve rooms at that one）。根據地圖，距離地鐵站最近的飯店為 (C)。

[36-38]

M Hello and welcome to the Gaming and Digital Entertainment Expo here in Santa Fe. My name is Jarvis O'Brien, and I am a product designer at Good Beats, INC. I am here to talk about our newest product: a fully functional and completely waterproof Bluetooth headphone set. Now, I know that there are plenty of Bluetooth audio devices on the market, but our product is different because it is designed to be used while swimming. The patented ear strap is not only comfortable, but it also prevents the headphones from falling off even during intense swims. That way, you can listen to your favorite music in or out of the water.

男 哈囉，歡迎光臨在聖菲這裡舉辦的遊戲與數位娛樂博覽會。我是賈維斯・歐布萊恩，是好節拍公司的產品設計師。我今天要談的是我們的最新產品：功能齊全、完全防水的藍牙耳機組。我知道現在市面上有很多藍牙音響設備，但我們的產品不一樣，因為它是設計成游泳專用的。我們的專利耳帶不但戴起來舒適，也能防止耳機掉落，就算在劇烈游泳時也一樣。如此一來，你在水中或離水後，都能聽到你最愛的音樂。

字彙 waterproof 防水的　device 設備
patented 獲得專利的　fall off 掉落
intense 劇烈的

36

說話者是誰？

(A) 好節拍公司的老闆

(B) 活動的籌辦者

(C) 一位產品設計師

(D) 一位產品經理

解析

說話者表示自己是 Good Beats（好節拍公司）的產品設計師（I am a product designer at Good Beats, INC.），因此答案為 (C)。

37

討論的產品為何？

(A) 耳機

(B) 手機

(C) 電腦遊戲

(D) 健身手環

說話者表示要介紹一下最新產品：防水藍牙耳機組（I am here to talk about our newest product: a fully functional and completely waterproof Bluetooth headphone set），因此答案為 (A)。

38

這項產品特別之處為何？
(A) 產品價格令人滿意。
(B) 產品防水。
(C) 產品有額外的新功能。
(D) 產品保固免費延長。

解析

說話者表示新產品在設計方面，讓人能夠於游泳時使用（it is designed to be used while swimming），因此答案為 (B)。

[39-41]

M Recently, we installed new software on all our computers. I hear some of you are having trouble since it has a lot of new features. So I asked Jeremy from the IT Department to help us. He will be giving several training sessions. Luckily, he will be available for us until we feel completely comfortable using the software. Please make sure to sign up for one of the training sessions.

男 最近，我們在所有電腦上都安裝了新軟體。因為軟體有很多新功能，我聽說你們有些人遇到了困難，因此我請了資訊科技部的傑瑞米來協助大家。他會給大家上幾堂訓練課程。很幸運的，他會一直協助我們，直到我們在軟體的使用上都完全輕鬆自在為止。請務必報名參加任何一堂訓練課程。

字彙 install 安裝　feature 功能、特色
comfortable 輕鬆自在的
sign up for 報名參加

39

根據說話者所說的內容，最近發生了什麼事？
(A) 舉行了一場資訊科技研討會。
(B) 有些政策改變了。
(C) 僱用了一位新技術人員。
(D) 安裝了某個軟體。

解析

獨白開頭提到最近為電腦安裝了新軟體（Recently, we installed new software on all our computers），因此答案為 (D)。

40

傑瑞米被要求做什麼？
(A) 刪除某個舊軟體
(B) 提供軟體訓練課程
(C) 購買某個新軟體
(D) 在辦公室待一陣子

解析

說話者表示已經向 Jeremy（傑瑞米）尋求協助，他會提供訓練課程（I asked Jeremy from the IT Department to help us），因此答案為 (B)。

41

聽眾被建議做什麼？
(A) 報名一堂訓練課程
(B) 要求傑瑞米親自過來幫忙
(C) 安裝某個新軟體
(D) 參加一場資訊科技研討會

解析

獨白的最後一段中，說話者建議從中選擇一堂訓練課程報名（Please make sure to sign up for one of the training sessions），因此答案應選 (A)。

[42-44]

W Hello, everyone. Thank you all for coming to the staff meeting. First, I would like to let you know that we will be moving to the Roosevelt Building on Lewis Street. I think this is the right decision since the Roosevelt Building is right across from the subway station. This will make your commutes much more convenient. But the downside is that we will have to pay a higher rent in the new building, so I would like to talk about how we can save a little more on other things.

女 哈囉各位，謝謝大家來參加員工會議。首先，我要告訴你們，我們即將搬到路易斯街上的羅斯福大樓。我認為這是個正確的決定，因為羅斯福大樓就在地鐵站的對面，這會讓你們上下班通勤更為方便。但這樣做也有缺點，就是我們在新大樓必須支付較高的租金。因此，我想要談談我們如何能在其他方面再節省一點。

字彙 across from 在……的對面　commute 通勤
　　　downside 缺點

42

這段說明的主旨為何？
(A) 下一年度的預算
(B) 即將進行的搬遷
(C) 大眾運輸
(D) 公司一項新的政策

解析

說話者告訴大家辦公室將搬到 Roosevelt Building
（羅斯福大樓）（I would like to let you know that
we will be moving to the Roosevelt Building），因
此答案為 (B)。

43

說話者說「我認為這是個正確的決定」，意思為何？
(A) 新的促銷很成功。
(B) 新的地點很方便。
(C) 僱用更多員工是個好選擇。
(D) 租這間辦公室公司花得比較少。

解析

女子提到 Roosevelt Building（羅斯福大樓）位在
地鐵站對面（the Roosevelt Building is right across
from the subway station），接著表示上下班將更方
便，因此答案為 (B)。

44

說話者接下來有可能做什麼？
(A) 討論一些省錢的方法
(B) 分享有關提升業績方法的點子
(C) 提供有關新地點的詳細資訊
(D) 仔細審核預算案

解析

獨白的最後一段，說話者表示要討論一下如何從其他
地方節省開支（I would like to talk about how we
can save a little more on other things），因此答案
為 (A)。

[45-47]

W Attention, customers. Welcome to our
store. Currently, we are having a big sale
in celebration of our 10th anniversary. This
sale will last until January 15. You can save
on almost every item in the store since we
are offering 30 to 50% discounts. You can
also enter our lucky drawing with every
purchase of more than 100 dollars. You may
win two plane tickets to Miami or a $200 gift
certificate. Don't miss this chance. We hope
you enjoy shopping here.

女 各位顧客請注意。歡迎光臨本店。為了慶祝我
　們的十週年慶，我們目前正在舉行大型優惠活
　動。這次的活動會一直持續到 1 月 15 日，店
　內幾乎每一項商品都有五到七折的優惠，保
　證讓您荷包省省省。而且，每買一件 100 美元
　以上的商品，都可以參加幸運抽獎。您有機會
　獲得兩張飛往邁阿密的機票，或一張面額 200
　美元的禮券。別錯過這次機會，我們希望您在
　這裡買得開心。

字彙 currently 目前
　　　in celebration of 為了慶祝……　last 持續
　　　draw 抽獎　gift certificate 禮券

45

廣播的地點最有可能為何？
(A) 圖書館
(B) 健身房
(C) 商店
(D) 彩券行

解析

獨白前半段中，說話者表示歡迎顧客光臨本店（. . .
customers. Welcome to our store），由此可知此廣
播的場所為商店內。

46

說話者宣布了什麼？
(A) 盛大開幕
(B) 即將進行的整修
(C) 清倉大拍賣
(D) 慶祝活動

解析

說話者提到為慶祝十週年，目前正進行大型優惠活動
（we are having a big sale in celebration of our 10th
anniversary），因此答案為 (D)。

47

顧客在幸運抽獎中可以贏得什麼？

(A) 五折優惠
(B) 機票
(C) 現金獎
(D) 免費點心

解析

獨白中提到參加抽獎活動，便有機會獲得兩張飛往邁阿密的機票或 200 美元的禮券（You may win two plane tickets to Miami or a $200 gift certificate），因此答案為 (B)。

[48-50]

> W Hello, Mr. Parker. This is Billy's Office Furniture. I am calling about your order. I was reviewing your order and noticed that there was a small mistake when we issued your receipt. I realized that we charged you for an office table which you didn't actually order. In order to fix this problem, we would like you to call our customer service center with your credit card number. We are so sorry for the inconvenience, and we hope to do business with you again.

女 哈囉，派克先生，這裡是比利辦公家具。我打來是有關您的訂單一事。我正在審核您的訂單，然後注意到我們在開您的收據時犯了一個小錯誤。我發現，我們向您多收了一張您其實並沒訂購的辦公桌的錢。為了彌補這個問題，我們希望您能打電話給我們的客服中心，並提供您的信用卡卡號。我們非常抱歉造成您的不便，希望下次能再為您服務。

字彙 issue 開立（收據） receipt 收據
　　 charge 收費　 purchase 購買

比利辦公家具
百老匯大道179號
5月10日

品項	數量	單價
椅子	2	45美元
辦公桌	1	70美元
儲藏櫃	1	120美元

總計：280美元

48

這通電話的目的為何？

(A) 為了通知聽者有一項訂購的商品缺貨
(B) 下訂單再多訂購一些椅子
(C) 為了提供現行拍賣的資訊
(D) 為了告知收據有問題

解析

說話者表示發現收據上的訂購品項有問題而致電對方（I am calling about your order. I was reviewing your order and noticed that there was a small mistake），因此答案為 (D)。

49

派克先生被要求提供什麼資料？

(A) 訂單編號
(B) 信用卡資訊
(C) 購買證明
(D) 詳細聯絡方式

解析

說話者請 Mr. Parker（派克先生）打電話到客服中心告知信用卡卡號（we would like you to call our customer service center with your credit card number），因此答案應選 (B)。

50

請看圖表。將會有多少錢退回給聽者？

(A) 45 美元
(B) 70 美元
(C) 90 美元
(D) 120 美元

解析

Mr. Parker（派克先生）實際上並未訂購辦公桌，但仍被收取費用（I realized that we charged you for an office table which you didn't actually order）。根據表格內容，辦公桌的價格為 70 美元，因此答案為 (B)。